Endors

"Caroline shares her multidimensional journey through the mysterious and daunting world of Lyme to finding wellness and light! Along her healing path she gathers wisdom about how we are all energy and can heal in many different ways. There is always hope! These lessons have allowed her to unlock and share the secrets that can help you turn illness into vitality."

-Pamala Oslie, Best-selling Author and Consultant
www.AuraColors.com

"Heartfelt and courageous DeLoreto has crafted a book that is not only practical but truly inspiring. This is an invaluable resource for anyone struggling with Lyme Disease or chronic illness. She not only shares her story but puts her journey into an easy-to-follow plan to help you take back your life again."

-Kimberly Cole, TV Producer & Host, Cortell Digital, Lyme Survivor

"Beautifully written. Heart centered. Caroline leads you by the hand on a healing journey offering you the wisdom of her vast experience across many healing modalities."

-Shelley Greenbaum, MA, CCC, COM, RMT, Speech Pathologist,
Animal Reiki Practitioner
www.shelleygreenbaumanimalreikipractitioner.com

"Caroline's incredible journey from the 'shades of night' to the 'light of day' provides insights on how our Creator is indeed able to provide healing to each of us."

-Dawn Densmore-Parent, Author, Highgate Center, VT
http://www.godsamazingways.com

"A must-read for anyone experiencing Lyme disease. For those in Lyme's grip, Caroline's spiritual journey of self-discovery provides hope and inspiration for everyone."

-Chris Latham, DCN, CNS, CKNS
https://www.healwellnutrition.com

Praise For
From Lyme to Light

By Rachel Sarah Thurston
Author and Lyme/Mold/CIRS Chronic Illness Warrior

I've known Caroline personally for 19 years now. And I can say honestly that she is THE REAL DEAL. Caroline is, quite literally, a walking miracle. What she has been through in the past two decades would have broken the strongest of any of us. Yet she has continually gotten back up—again and again and again—through her sheer will, faith, unparalleled resilience, insatiable curiosity for research, and unwavering optimism around her own future presence on this planet.

Always the curious observer around her own ailments, Caroline is the very definition of true grit and perseverance. And through it all, she laughs, she smiles, and she says, "Oh well! What can I learn from this new challenge?"

She never gives up.

Caroline has a true gift in medical intuition allowing her to help people identify and overcome blocks in their healing that others might not pick up on. Her natural intuition combined with her vast education and experience in functional diagnostic nutrition, holistic medicine, and clinical psychology along with her deep passion and dedication to spiritual growth and practices make her a formidable ally. She excels at helping others identify health and energy deficits to rebuild their wellness on all levels.

In my darkest times along this journey healing from advanced Neurological Lyme Disease, MSIDS, and Mold Illness (CIRS), Caroline has been one of those angelic lights who has brought me hope, strength, and inspiration. She has lifted me up during those dark night-of-the-soul chapters. Those moments where I've no longer seen a way out nor a desire to continue on. She has been the bright light that helped me see the greater picture, offering encouragement and guidance when I most needed them.

It's clear to me that her purpose on this earth is to inspire, to spread love, and to give those of us facing similar battles hope as we move forward. *From Lyme to Light* captures the spirit of her optimism which we can drink from whenever we most need it!

I am grateful beyond words that she has been able to write a book which illuminates her own healing process. Many of the tools she's taught me (which she shares in this book) over the years have become indispensable to me along my own journey.

I am in total agreement with Caroline that having Lyme has the potential to elevate each of us onto a higher level of consciousness and awareness. It's clear when you read her words, that she is channeling a higher consciousness and intuitiveness. It all resonates so deeply for me from what I have experienced myself along this multifaceted, roller coaster voyage.

I have often wondered to myself, "How did she get to be so wise?!"

It's clear to me that—from having read her book and knowing her personally for almost two decades—Caroline is living into her greater soul's purpose: to give those of us in the world living with Lyme, both hope and guidance.

And that, my friends, is the most powerful light saber we can ever wield on this path.

Rachel Sarah Thurston
"State Of Sparkle"
Marketing & Branding Coaching/Consultant
Writer and Multimedia Storyteller
www.stateofsparkle.com / www.rachelsarahthurston.com

FROM
Lyme
TO
Light

FROM
Lyme
TO
Light

A SPIRITUAL JOURNEY AND GUIDE FOR HEALING FROM LYME DISEASE

CAROLINE L. DELORETO, FDN-P

FOREWORD BY DR. JENNIFER SALCIDO, ND

From Lyme to Light:
A Spiritual Journey and Guide for Healing from Lyme Disease

Catalyst for Change Publishing, LLC
Highgate Center, VT
www.catalystforchangepublishing.com

For information, address:

fromlymetolight@gmail.com
www.CarolineDeloreto.com

Every attempt has been made to source all quotes properly.

For additional copies or bulk purchases visit:
www.CarolineDeLoreto.com

Editors: Camilla La Mer and Adam Taft
Cover Design: Sam Aalam and Caroline DeLoreto
Art: Caroline DeLoreto
Interior Layout: Fusion Creative Works, fusioncw.com

Hardcover ISBN: 978-1-7378137-2-9
Paperback ISBN: 978-1-7378137-0-5

First Edition, 2022

Printed in the United States of America

Dedication

I dedicate this book to my loving partner Adam Taft and
niece Alicia Lopez for sticking by me through it all.

I would also like to honor and acknowledge all those who have lost
their life to Lyme disease or chronic illness, and send love and prayers
to those who love and miss them.

Disclaimer

Information in this book is not intended to treat, diagnose, cure, or prevent any disease. Information provided is for educational purposes only and represents the opinions formed by the author based on her experiences and review of numerous sources of information related to the subject matter. While I use reasonable efforts to provide accurate information, no warranties or representations are made as to the accuracy, validity, or reliability of any information presented. No responsibility is assumed for any errors or omissions in the content of this book or its associated materials. Information is not intended to serve as medical advice. Always seek the advice of a licensed health care provider before making any treatment decisions.

Contents

Foreword

"Will you teach your children what we have taught our children?
That the earth is our mother? What befalls the earth befalls the
sons of the earth. This we know that the earth does not belong to
man, man belongs to the earth. All things are connected like the
blood that unites us all. Man did not weave the web of life,
he is merely a strand in it. Whatever he does to the web,
he does to himself."

- Chief Seattle

Hello Dear Readers,

I have worked as a naturopathic doctor specializing in Lyme Disease treatment for over 15 years. I am so happy for you to have this valuable reference and resource at your fingertips. This book is like Caroline, a gem full of love, joy, beauty, and hope; a shining light that will help guide you so you can take shortcuts on your healing journey by following the path of someone who has been there before. Everyone is different and unique but learning from one another is a gift. This book is so generously full of nuggets you can gather from Caroline.

Even though Lyme disease can be a very difficult path, so many of my patients report being healthier after it than ever before by transforming from the inside out. *From Lyme to Light* can help you achieve this. I have learned so much from Caroline and her book. I can't wait to see the transformations you make after reading it and applying the principles to your life. With that said let me share a bit about my expertise and background with treating Lyme Disease.

But first I would like to share more about my background and thoughts on healing and how when we heal ourselves, we are helping heal the earth. I entered naturopathic medical school at Bastyr University in the fall of 2000 full of excitement. What drew me to naturopathic medicine were the principles. These principles are:

1. Do No Harm

2. The Healing Power of Nature

3. Prevention

4. Doctor as Teacher

5. Treat the Whole Person

6. Identify and Treat the Cause

Being an ND is a lifelong study and something I knew I would never get bored of. Bastyr University was a sight to behold in St. Edwards State Park in Kenmore, Washington, a suburb of Seattle. I was so eager to learn and I had many memorable teachers that kept classes engaging. I loved when our biochemistry professor would end class saying, "Come back tomorrow to learn more secrets of the universe."

One of my favorite professors was Dr. William Mitchell, ND, one of the founders of Bastyr University. He often talked about GAIA, Mother Earth. I remember feeling chills up and down my spine when he said, "You have been called here, you have a special mission. You are GAIA's immune system." Now this was something I never heard before but could get fully behind. Our Mother Earth needs protection, people looking out for her well-being and taking care of her as she takes care of us. During my six years at Bastyr University I learned all about herbal medicine, diet, nutrition, homeopathic remedies, hydrotherapy, physiotherapy, pharmacology, counseling, and more.

So much of what we use as medicine comes from the Earth, so we have to take care of her.

"You have been called here, you have a special mission. You are GAIA's immune system."

My Introduction and Training in Lyme Disease

In my last year of school I attended a Grand Rounds by a recent naturopathic graduate who had Lyme disease. I had learned a little bit about Lyme in Infectious Disease class but really hadn't scratched the surface. I went up to the speaker after the presentation because I was fascinated with what she was sharing. She said, "If you really want to learn about Lyme disease you need to study with Dr. Dietrich Klinghardt (MD)." Dr Klinghardt's name came up again a few weeks later as I was completing an internship with a leading naturopathic doctor in Seattle. I knew for my upcoming residency I would need to expand my injection skills so I asked her for advice. She said, "If you really want to learn about injections you need to study with Dr. Dietrich Klinghardt (MD)." This caught my attention. I had never heard of this Dr. Klinghardt but in a short time frame two doctors I admired told me the same thing, "You need to study with Dr. Klinghardt." I looked him up and luckily for me he was teaching an upcoming injection class called Neuraltherapy nearby. I signed up for the class and soon found out what all the buzz was about.

Dr. Klinghardt is a renaissance man of a doctor, able to treat all kinds of harrowing conditions with his vast tool box, and especially the needle. He did all kinds of injections that were above and beyond anything I had encountered in my training. Neuraltherapy is one of his specialties and involves puncturing the skin and injecting Procaine to affect the nerves and in turn the organs they are connected to. As I was listening to Dr. Klinghardt explain the technique and how it works it reminded me of a story I hoped to share with him of my first trip to Mexico a few years earlier when a Mayan shaman punctured the skin over my abdomen with a snake tooth. I had gone to the ER the day before but still wasn't feeling great. My friend thought I was crazy but I was willing to do anything to feel better at that point and it worked!

It was time for the lunch break and at Dr. Klinghardt's seminars there is usually a mob of people surrounding him at each break. The group dwindled down to just he and I and as I started telling him about my Mexican adventure he invited me for lunch. We had a great time chatting and near the end of our lunch he told me he was looking for an assistant and asked if I was interested in working for him. Wow! What a wonderful opportunity except that I already had a job as a resident at a naturopathic college. At the time there were only a few coveted residency positions that students competed for so I felt fortunate to have been selected. It took some soul searching but I decided working with Dr. Klinghardt was an opportunity I couldn't pass up.

At Dr. Klinghardt's office I assisted him with energetic testing and provided some of the neuraltherapy injections his patients required. Many of them had chronic degenerative neurological diseases such as MS, ALS, Lyme disease, and autism. At the time Dr. Klinghardt was being filmed for a groundbreaking documentary about Lyme disease called Under Our Skin. I met some of the patients featured in the film and along with the other patients at the office they really blew me away in terms of their talents, intelligence, sensitivity, caring, persistence, resourcefulness, and resilience. I remember one day philosophizing with Dr. Klinghardt about why it could be that such wonderful people end up with such a dreadful debilitating disease. Dr. Klinghardt talked about global warming and how the ticks that carry the disease were not being killed off by colder temperatures as they used to be. I wondered on a spiritual level if it was a way to keep people out of the wilderness and to keep the wilderness wild. Dr. Klinghardt said yeah but people with Lyme usually love the outdoors and take good care of it. We were quiet for a while and then I remembered Dr. Mitchell and the calling to be part of GAIA's immune system. Many times when people get sick the first thing they do is start cleaning up their environment. They throw out the chemicals, buy organic food, and get air and water purifiers. All of these strategies are great for healing a person but they are also healing for the planet.

I have always been an environmentalist at heart. Environmental medicine is the study of how our environment affects our health and it is no secret that the more polluted the air, water, and soil is the more polluted our food is and the harder it is to be healthy. We all need to be part of GAIA's immune system if we want to have health for ourselves, our children, and our children's children. We are connected to Mother Earth. Her fate and our fate are intertwined.

> *"Many times when people get sick the first thing they do is start cleaning up their environment. They throw out the chemicals, buy organic food, and get air and water purifiers. All of these strategies are great for healing the person but they are also healing for the planet...We are all part of GAIAs immune system."*

Dr. Klinghard is a master of many types of healing. He can do all kinds of injections, some surface level, some deep within the body. He knows all about the use of natural remedies as well as pharmaceuticals and dietary strategies. He was teaching about mold, heavy metals, parasites, and EMFs before it was en vogue. He is a charismatic doctor that attracts quite a following and a genius regarding the human body. But what I found most profound about his work was how he weaved in healing on the emotional, psychological, and even ancestral levels. Dr. Klinghard treats the whole person, the goal of every naturopathic doctor, and I learned a lot from him.

After working with Dr. Klinghardt I had this strong feeling inside that I was supposed to be somewhere really beautiful. I had lived in beautiful areas but something told me there is a place even more beautiful and you need to go there. As I was traveling down the West Coast I stopped in Santa Barbara, California and had a deep knowing. This is the beautiful place where you are supposed to be. I worked with a wonderful MD, Dr. Scott Saunders, and eventually started my own practice, Santa Barbara Integrative Medicine.

Just as in the days of working in Seattle with Dr. Klinghardt I was also blown away by my patients with Lyme disease. One of those patients was Caroline DeLoreto. Talk about gifts and skills. Caroline is not only a teacher and a Licensed Marriage and Family Therapist (LMFT), she is also gifted with the ability to see deeper patterns and meanings in physical symptoms that are beyond what meets the eye. A person can study and read about a condition but the best teacher is through experience. Caroline has been in the trenches fighting Lyme and learning what works and what doesn't. This book is beyond the standard list of protocols. Caroline's "Diamond of Healing Philosophy" is a "Treat the Whole Person" approach that is so refreshing to see. You can use it as a guide to find areas you need to focus on in your own healing journey.

Caroline is an inspiration. She is continually amazing me with her endeavors. She is one of those people who really stands out. Even in the midst of her battle with Lyme disease she seemed to be full of energy, a smile on her face, and a sparkle in her eye. She has come full circle and is now giving back to the Lyme community with her knowledge, experience, insight, and caring.

Never give up and enjoy these nuggets of wisdom on healing throughout this book. I know I have. Thank you for working on healing yourself and in return helping to heal the earth. A win-win for everyone!

All the best to you on your healing journey,

Dr. Jennifer Salcido, ND
www.sbintegrative.com

PART I

Incorrect Diagnosis:
My Story From Lyme to Light

Preface: Incorrect Diagnosis

"I'm sorry, Caroline, you have early onset dementia. It looks to be rapid onset. There isn't much we can do. There really isn't treatment."

The words reverberated through me, covering every inch of my mind, body, and soul. I was thirty-two years old, and I had my whole life ahead of me. How could this be?

The words bounced off me—I wasn't willing to take these ones on. The doctor continued, "The good news is you won't remember soon enough."

Real funny I thought.

"You might want to get your affairs in order now."

My affairs? I couldn't care less about my affairs. I wanted my life back and I wasn't ready to give up yet. Oh great, I thought, now I'm really alone in trying to figure out what's been causing the complete melt-down in my brain, nervous system, and body over the past year. Now they've stuck me under one of their "untouchable" umbrella diagnoses.

"It's not treatable," the doctor said. "There is nothing you can do."

When you hear these words, become alert—this usually isn't actually true. You can always do something to help yourself! They just don't know what to tell you.

There is usually an underlying cause (or causes) to most conditions that can at least help you get better or extend your life. Allopathic Medicine just doesn't focus on finding the cause of most diseases. Allopathic doctors focus instead on categorizing you with a diagnosis and then medicating to treat symptoms, not causes. It takes work to get to causes. It isn't always just physical either. It can be emotional, mental, spiritual, or energetic; usually a combo of all of these. That takes time to figure out and, honestly, doctors don't have *that* time when they are limited to 15-30 minute appointments for insurance and the organizations they work for. So overall we end up in a system where there is time to give medications out to treat symptoms so the patient feels better. This is a bandage, not treating root causes. Pharmaceutical companies make more money off treating symptoms than getting to the cause of them because you would no longer need the medication if you fix the problem causing it, and that is not good financial business for the companies running the industry.

Don't get me wrong, I am thankful for all the medication options we have, and I use pharmaceuticals when needed with gratitude. It's when they become such an influence on how doctors practice medicine and treat patients that it becomes a problem. You always want to be awake to this because, as you know, *money talks*. This is why we have to become alert, ask questions, continue to seek answers even if one doctor has given up on you! Take action and do whatever you can to support your body when you become ill and out of balance.

Diagnoses are labels. Labels are quite limiting when we think and believe we *are* the diagnosis, not that we *have* a diagnosis. Remember, the diagnosis can change and honestly there usually is something you can do to help yourself heal.

Others say they feel relief when they receive their diagnosis. For me, I felt anything but relief on this one. I felt more alone, further away from finding the help I needed in figuring out what was causing my neurological breakdown; something had to be at the root of it! I wasn't like this just ten months earlier. Instead I was teaching and leading mountain bike trips with middle school kids, I was running a private practice as a therapist with kids and families, and I was able to walk and talk with no issues. All of that life had melted away so quickly!

Instead of searching for the underlying trigger that caused these outer symptoms of neurological decline and dementia, my doctor gave up on searching for an answer, so it must be game over. I'll just have dementia the rest of my life, and die from it soon, and they think that is "OK"?

No, for me, the changes in my brain and the loss of control over my physical body were not OK. They were downright scary each and every day with weird, painful sensations all over my body, including the inability to walk and changes in vision, sound, and touch. Let's not forget the falls, tremors, and memory loss . . . But for some reason, no matter how much I told doctors about these symptoms, the summary reports for my visits always looked the same: "Client denies having tremors, no walking difficulties, no past history of infections." WTF? Yes to all. If you don't fit in the box, they squeeze you in it! You become invisible or "crazy."

Little did they know when they gave me this diagnosis that, in less than three months, I would be dead.

Yes, dead.

But not from early rapid onset dementia, yet from something much more treatable: neurological Lyme disease.

The Guest House

By Rumi

This being human is a guest house.
Every morning a new arrival.

A joy, a depression, a meanness,
some momentary awareness comes
as an unexpected visitor.

Welcome and entertain them all!
Even if they're a crowd of sorrows,
who violently sweep your house
empty of its furniture,
still, treat each guest honorably.
He may be clearing you out
for some new delight.

The dark thought, the shame, the malice,
meet them at the door laughing,
and invite them in.

Be grateful for whoever comes,
because each has been sent
as a guide from beyond.

1

Introduction

Dear Reader,

This book, *From Lyme to Light: A Spiritual Journey and Guide to Healing from Lyme Disease*, tells the story of my near-death experience after having a stroke from undiagnosed neurological Lyme disease. Now, five years later, I have gone from having debilitating Lyme . . . to Light! I have healed and I am living in a state of better health and wellness than I was before I got sick.

I chose to write this book to give back in a positive way by being of service and giving the light and hope to others that I found while reading books and blogs about Lyme disease while I was so sick. This is something I CAN do. I encourage you to find the things that you CAN do and spend time on sharing those things instead of focusing on all the ways Lyme has robbed you of your "before Lyme life" and what you USED TO BE ABLE TO DO. It's one heck of a journey, but it's worth it—and it requires learning to live in the moment, in the now, and doing what you can to be present, have fun, be kind, contribute, and share love. Please know shining your authentic light AS YOU ARE is ENOUGH. You are loved, you have purpose, and just practicing being peaceful and "as you are" is enough.

In this book, I also focus on the "energy body" and how energy is a key player in our ability to physically heal and overcome Lyme and other chronic illness challenges. I will address environmental factors like mold, toxins, infections, and herbs and how all these things carry their own frequencies that interact with our physical body and energy field. We have a lot of choices and power in our healing journeys, and we all have the innate ability to heal ourselves and choose life, especially with the help of finding a spiritual connection to the higher power that be. I will also introduce my Diamond of Healing Philosophy in Part II as a tool to help you assess where in your own journey you may need to focus in on to heal.

It isn't always easy, that's for sure, but I want this book to be an inspiration and motivator to awaken your internal drive to be well and present. I hope that it gives a message of personal empowerment around taking back your health and wellness.

I want this book to act as a catalyst in your healing and spiritual growth, acting like a lightning bolt and jolting you into awareness on your journey when you may have lost hope or are looking for your purpose when you are struggling with Lyme disease or any other chronic illness. It's your body, your health, and your responsibility to do the work to heal—no one else's. Doctors can't do it for you. Once you realize and fully own this, you will be unstoppable!

I'm here to empower you to take back your life, your health, your wellness, and choose the energy frequency you want to live in. Yes, it is a choice!

I will take the time to share practical tools, exercises, and experiences that helped me to heal faster. I will share easy and affordable tools you can use at home to support the healing of your physical body. I will also share ideas that worked for me on my journey in the hope that it may inspire your own healing and awakening on your path to health and wellness.

Invitation to You

I hope that you, in turn, will share with me your journey and lessons after reading this book. Please send me a letter or email any time with your journey. I would love to hear about you and your awakenings and challenges and hardships with Lyme. By going to my website www.CarolineDeloreto.com, you can email or snail mail me anything you want to share. I will personally reply to you because you are important, and you matter. You have purpose and are loved! We all are. If you would like to be added to the prayer list for healing, you can do that on the site too.

I hope you enjoy this journey with me as you read and that you will join me in helping raise the frequency and vibration of our world to one of love and light and wellness. If each of us can start by changing ourselves from the inside-out, connecting to our higher selves and an awareness of the power and peace of a higher purpose and God, we could have peace and love on Earth. It starts within each of us. Each of us matters, and our choices and the changes we make on the inside changes everything around us, since we are all energy. If each of us are vibrating at a higher frequency of love, joy, peace, and so on, then everywhere we go the frequency of our energy helps shift the environments we visit and helps shift the world to one of more conscious and loving higher-frequency living.

This is where true healing and wellness begins—and sticks. You can't have the lower frequency of illness in you if you learn to stay at an internal healing-state vibration of love and inner peace. But since we are human and aren't perfect, we will have stress and ups and downs, so it's important to learn tools to help empower each of us to quickly shift ourselves back into a healing state. That is key to wellbeing and optimal health. I honor you on your path and pray for your healing and light each day.

To the journey! With gratitude,

Caroline DeLoreto

PS: You can go to my website for more information on topics around Lyme, inspirational speaking events, future books, and other services. Go to: www.CarolineDeloreto.com

PART I

SECTION 1

My Stroke of Neurolyme

The Road Not Taken

By Robert Frost

Two roads diverged in a yellow wood,
And sorry I could not travel both
And be one traveler, long I stood
And looked down one as far as I could
To where it bent in the undergrowth;

Then took the other, as just as fair,
And having perhaps the better claim,
Because it was grassy and wanted wear;
Though as for that the passing there
Had worn them really about the same,

And both that morning equally lay
In leaves no step had trodden black.
Oh, I kept the first for another day!
Yet knowing how way leads on to way,
I doubted if I should ever come back.

I shall be telling this with a sigh
Somewhere ages and ages hence:

Two roads diverged in a wood, and I—
I took the one less traveled by,
And that has made all the difference.

2

My Stroke of Neurolyme

On April 15th, 2016, at 8:00 p.m. PDT, I sat in my comfy chair with my husband, Adam, watching our favorite TV series on Netflix. It had been a "good brain" day overall, and I had actually even gone for my first short jog in months. We were watching our show like we always did when all of a sudden I had the sharpest stabbing pain behind my left eyeball, like a knife had been stuck in the left side of my skull above my ear. I stood straight up, grabbing at my head and screaming in pain, and Adam jumped up too. Something big was wrong, and I knew it to my core. All in the same moment, I had to poop and pee but I couldn't figure out where the bathroom was or how to get there, so Adam picked me up and carried me quickly to the toilet where I instantly did both things. Once I finished and went to stand up, my right leg gave out. I stammered, "Hospital, now!! Str . . . store . . . stroke!" I could no longer stand on my right leg or use my right arm.

But then the craziest thing happened. In that same moment, all the fog and dementia confusion I had been in for the past ten months disappeared and I could think clear and fast and understand what was happening around me, but I was unable to move my body correctly.

Adam carried me to the car, drove me to the hospital a block away, and carried me into the ER. When I went to speak, I realized I no longer could. Suddenly all the word centers of my brain around the ability to process and understand words were extremely heightened but I was unable to verbally communicate any of what I was experiencing since that area was compromised. I had also acquired a severe stutter, and it was extremely frustrating and humorous at the same time, causing me to go into giggles on one side of my face.

The ER staff immediately threw me on a stretcher and the ER doctor ran all the stroke tests on me. He pronounced that I was having a full-blown stroke and, since they didn't have an MRI machine or equipment for treating a stroke at this hospital, he told me that I needed to be transferred to the main downtown hospital ASAP.

While this went on, I kept thinking I could still do everything normally and would be shocked that my right side wasn't responding. When I thought I was using my right hand, my left hand would be doing it instead! My dominant hand had somehow flipped, and I was suddenly left-handed! Doctors wouldn't believe us when Adam told them, "She is right-handed, not left, this isn't normal." I stayed left-hand dominant for about two months.

Long story short, I was transferred after two shift changes (and a long wait) to the downtown hospital for a bed in the neurology wing. The neurologist had stayed up all night waiting for me but had just gone home for the weekend when I finally arrived, so I did not see a neurologist for the four days I was in the hospital. I received pretty poor care for the first two days in the neurology department, with many of the nurses thinking I was "faking it" since I looked too young to have a stroke (these were their words, which they said because they thought I couldn't understand them since I couldn't speak). They didn't take very good care of me even with Adam staying on them. I became very dehydrated.

At 10:00 a.m. on Sunday morning I was wheeled out of my room to have an MRI scan to check the damage the stroke had caused. I had woken up feeling really off and wrong, but without being able to speak it was hard to communicate what I was feeling to anyone. This was the scariest part with the stroke; not being able to communicate but being so aware on the inside. It was sort of like being trapped inside my own body with no control to steer it.

As they wheeled me out away from Adam, I could remember thinking something is not right with me, I am not OK, but there was nothing I could do but surrender.

With all my treatments over the past ten months, and with a brain tumor in 2011, I had gotten pretty used to getting MRI scans. I had done over 45 of them in total with no problems; I actually found them relaxing. I was lifted from the gurney and put in the MRI because I couldn't move myself yet. Everything seemed pretty normal other than I still felt sort of out of it and sick. I went inside the MRI machine and it started up.

Click, click, click . . . The sounds of the machine were familiar, but then suddenly everything went silent.

Next thing I knew, I was leaving Earth. I was dying.

3

Near Death –
I Have More to Do on Earth, Please!

The next thing I knew, I was leaving Earth, and the speed was multiplying. I was getting sucked up and up and up into the sky away from Earth. It was like I was one of those Stretch Armstrong dolls and my feet were extremely tiny way down inside the MRI machine, and I was way up off the earth getting sucked into the universe. It was black with lots of shimmering lights, colored energies, and star-looking things all around me, and all I could think was "I am not ready to leave Earth yet."

So I started pleading with the universe, "No, I am not ready to leave Earth yet. I have more to do! Please, I am not ready! I have more to do on Earth!"

But on and on I continued to get sucked upwards away from Earth, and I knew I wasn't there any longer, but I wasn't willing to give up on it.

"I am not ready to leave yet! I have more to do! Please listen to me!"

And in that moment, everything paused. The stillness could have been a second or ten minutes—there was no such thing as time where I was, so simultaneously (as I was in total stillness, like someone hit the pause button) a bunch of information and actions took place. Since I was off Earth in this other space, time didn't work like it does down here on Earth. It all sort of happened at once.

I looked down to where my feet had been and they were miles upon miles below me, now little dots. My soul stretched out for eternity above it. I was sort of slowing down now and there was some sort of interaction I had where I was being cleaned up energetically and something was being decided. It was all shades of light and energy.

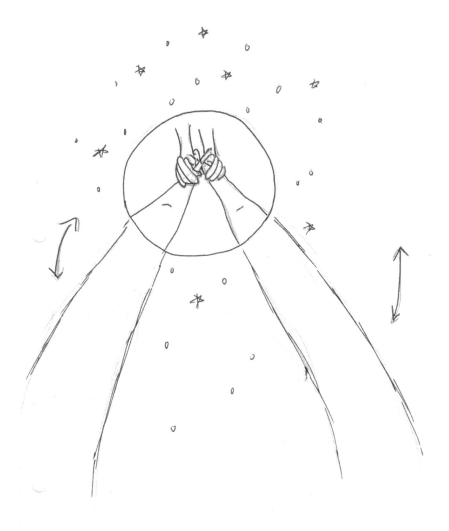

"I am not ready to go, please!" I pleaded again.

Suddenly, the face of my mentor back on Earth in a spirit form—who had been my biggest support throughout my illness and total health collapse the year leading into this moment—appeared and two huge hands of "his" grabbed my ankles way below and I heard a voice say, "No, you're not!" (Referring to it's not my time to leave Earth yet). And with both big hands on my ankles, "he" whipped me back down to where my physical body lay limp and, with a slam, my spirit/energy body went back into my physical body in the MRI machine. At the same exact moment that I saw "his" face looking up at me and felt "his" hands on my feet and he whipped me down, a blue-colored version of me was peeled away completely—from my feet first, up to my head. It was like a cookie-cutter version of me had been peeled off; I tried to grab my peeled-off self to carry it back down with me, but I wasn't allowed to. The last thing to detach was the hands—I held my blue self as tightly as I could, but it was no use. Off and away it went as I was slammed back to the earth. A huge part of me had died and wasn't allowed to return, and there was nothing I could do to stop it.

At the very same moment as my mentor's face appeared and my old self peeled away, I received a visual download with a bunch of information in the form of pictures and images and thoughts. It felt as if it moved as fast as the speed of light. So fast! The message I received as I traveled back down into my body at what felt like 100 miles per hour was that I was to help people and society better understand Lyme disease and chronic illnesses and help others find healing. There was another way besides what was already going on in Allopathic medicine. I was to help people see Lyme in a new light. This was the new theme and my soul's new purpose in my new life.

BAM! The next thing I knew, I was slammed back into my physical body and the MRI machine completely malfunctioned and had an electrical power surge. It literally flashed and shut off completely.

The MRI technician came and pulled me out, "Ma'am, are you ok? I have never seen the MRI machine do anything like that before. I don't understand what could have caused it to turn itself off like that or electrically do what it just did. It wasn't you . . ."

Oh but *it was*, I thought to myself.

"You were perfectly still with no movement whatsoever the last ten minutes, so it wasn't you that did this. I am so sorry, I have to reboot the whole machine, which will take another fifteen minutes and then restart your scan all over again. Hang tight while I get this thing back up and running."

I knew what had happened. I had died and fallen back to Earth. Back into my body!

I wanted to say something but I had no way to speak with the stutter I had from the stroke. Even if I could have, I wouldn't have been able to say "it" out loud—not yet, not for a few months—to another living soul.

I had died and been reborn. Part of me was still gone and hadn't returned, and I immediately knew the moment I landed back on Earth that something was missing and different inside me. The blue part of me that did not return with me was what I now call "old Caroline." The first difference I noticed most drastically was that all the purpose inside of me for teaching or helping kids, which I'd had since as early as I can remember, was completely gone. Missing. Dead. I was told that I had completed that life and it was done.

I was given a new purpose and plan in the same physical body since I had begged to stay on Earth. I did a soul path switch in a way to start another learning experience at a soul level. But even more than that, I knew I wanted to be on Earth still because I was excited about the shift we are going through right now into a more heart-based planet. We are moving from duality to a heart-based light and love frequency, and I am here to help with this shift. Instead of doing it with kids, now I am here in my new life to do it in medicine and help people ignite their own inner healing abilities and empower them to overcome chronic illness like Lyme and all the other things showing up as we as a planet go through this shift. I got downloads of what I was going to be doing purpose-wise really clearly, and I was a completely different person than I was ten minutes earlier before dying (purpose and focus-wise). God gave me a new calling, or added calling, for this lifetime.

Back in my body, I lay in the cold air of the hospital waiting for the MRI to reboot, not knowing what the sensations on my skin meant—not knowing it was cold. All I remember was none of my senses made sense to me. I literally felt like a baby being born into the world all over again. My ability to control my sensory input was zero, so everything came in at the same loudness—my eyes couldn't understand how to adjust to light or processes what they were seeing. It was like I could hear a word for what things were in my head when I looked at it, but it felt like I was seeing them for the first time in my life. Brand new in a 3-D world.

Brand New in a 3-D World

As I was thrown back into my body and arrived, I received yet another set of three downloads. They were very specific clear messages/directions and I could see and understand all of them. The first one was an image and lots of information on writing contracts—spiritual ones. I was to focus first on rewriting contracts with all the people in my life if I was going to live. The second was of a woman doctor, and I was going to be working with her in medicine in this life. The third was of lots of books—writing books, reading books, and helping people heal through writing. I will be going more in depth about these three downloads and how they unfolded in the past five years in chapter 4.

When I arrived back in my body, it felt as though I had never been in a body before, or like it had been a very long time. I recognized I was in a body but it felt brand new to be inside a body—using a hand, for example, or perceiving the world around me.

My nervous system had been completely reset. All past emotional triggers were gone. I could still sense that the neuron wiring for the triggers lay just under the surface, and I knew that if I didn't take the time away from "old Caroline's" daily life to be quiet and allow the reset to take, they would begin to fire again. I was given such a big gift of no longer having the charged triggers from my past that had stopped me from fully living in the moment. I was literally being given a new life, a new nervous system, and a new start like a baby. I knew this the minute I arrived back in my body.

Since the near-death experience, instead of having prior memories that I can feel in my body, they come back as filmstrips that spin around my head and body. They look like a filmstrip of someone else's life, but it's mine. All the memories I've made after April 17, 2016 (my re-birthday) play as first-person like my old ones used to. I am seeing those memories from my eyes, not watching myself from afar on a screen. This really helps with the nervous system reset. If I am watching my memories and not experiencing them first-hand, I am less emotionally triggered. It's almost like the vipassana meditation where you watch yourself on a movie screen to become emotionally detached and learn to stay awake.

I saw and communicated in pictures for the first year instead of communicating with language. Everywhere I went, I received images and pictures from the people I was with—they came as what I call "downloads" and they were fast and full of so much information. Downloads can come in the form of pictures/images, hearing words, or feelings in the body—aware that you just know something suddenly that's accurate and correct, but not knowing how you know. To me, downloads are God's/the spirit realm's way of communicating with us.

I would become so overwhelmed by these intense downloads everywhere I went from all people I met or saw on the street. I wasn't able to filter them out yet; all the information and pictures around people just flowed, and I heard and saw them without trying. With my brain being so sick with pathogens form neurological Lyme and Bartonella, which is one of the many co-infections of Lyme, I couldn't keep up processing the downloads. Instead I avoided crowds and people as much as I could the first four years after the stroke, until I was stronger and healthier. Taking an introduction class on intuition taught me how to create a boundary with this heightened sense that had turned on after the near-death, and I learned how to increase my grounding and my auric boundary (energy field boundary). It worked! I don't get all that information just walking around any longer as it's filtered now, but I know it is always there. I can choose to go into a meditation and re-open it, but it doesn't help me health-wise to have that on all the time. We are all unconsciously getting information from each other, spirit, and God in all we do. More on this later in this book.

I understood why I was shown that my first task was to rewrite contracts with all those in my life. I had a fresh start, a completely new purpose focused on healing and medicine and Lyme instead of children and teaching, and I needed to live very differently from who I had been, a Type A "go-go" personality, to sustain this very stressed-out physical body I was back inside. I had died from an adrenal crisis—STRESS. Chronic, acute, sustained, PTSD, illness—STRESS. Not the stroke or the Lyme by themselves. It had been the way "old Caroline" ran— she lived on her adrenals to focus and ramp up and get through her very busy and exciting life, and to survive her childhood and family life too. STRESS was at the base of why the Lyme disease had wreaked such havoc on my body. A lot of us who get chronic Lyme usually have to go through a lifestyle change to get better. Living more balanced and creating boundaries and healthy lifestyles is a huge step, and it's not always something that feels good or familiar for caretakers or Type A people.

In the end, the near-death gave me many gifts for living life more fully and in the present moment, so I am thankful for it.

4

The Three Downloads

As I shared earlier, I had three specific downloads about my new purpose when I landed back inside my body on Earth. I want to give you an overview of each one here.

1. Rewrite Contracts with Others in Your Life

The first image "download" I was given when I came back into my body was a large scroll with a feather pen writing on it. It read "Contracts" at the top of the page. I also received a download of rewriting contracts with all those in my life to stay alive and heal. I knew I must literally and figuratively look at the energy balances and exchanges with those people whom I spent my time and energy with and make sure they were balanced. I had to clean them up if they were not, and rewrite the role of both myself and the others in my life if our relationship was no longer healthy and balanced. This was the first thing I was supposed to do in my new life after the rebirth, and my health relied on it. If I didn't do this, it would be game over all over again. All of this came in the form of pictures, cartoons, and downloaded information that I can only explain as suddenly just knowing something very clearly. That is how I got my more detailed instructions, through a knowing download.

This was the first task I was to focus on when I was well enough, and I began my contract rewriting about three weeks after getting out of the hospital. This process took about two years to complete. When I finished, I received a call a week or so later that initiated the start of my second download. It was pretty cool to experience these in real life after receiving them as images years before.

See the next chapter to learn more about the process of rewriting contracts and see if it could be helpful for you to do in your healing journey from Lyme disease too.

2. Working with a Woman Doctor

Working with...
—Collaborating—

The second download was of this beautiful woman doctor who I was sitting with and learning from her as she worked with her patients. I saw an image of her, and she turned and looked up at me and then I saw myself working with her in medicine, doing something with Lyme disease and chronic illnesses. As I shared earlier in the book, three years later a doctor called me and asked if I would come work with her and train to one day take over her business as a bioenergetic tester and health coach specializing in helping those with Lyme disease.

A month later, in early February, my partner Adam and I flew out to Vermont in the dead of winter to meet her. I hadn't traveled outside of California since the stroke because my brain fatigue would be triggered with any new experience. New things would put me in sensory overload and I would "spin out" and feel completely lost and exhausted. This was the next step in my healing—we planned a four-day trip to Vermont to see how it would go training with her.

When I met her, there was an energetic synergy that lit up inside me almost like a clear sign that this was important—pay attention! When I got out of the car in the dark of the evening and she took my hand and walked me over the icy porch to her house, I looked up to meet her in person for the first time and I knew! It was her! The beautiful woman doctor in the download from three years earlier! I had never seen her in person, I had only spoken to her on the phone a dozen times. This was the first actual meeting. And I had never seen what she looked like.

I was officially on the second download in my new life path, and it had begun. I had found her and she had found me. What was to unfold next, I had no idea—other than I was on the right next step on my new life path ahead and healing! Three months later, Adam and I had packed up our life in Santa Barbara, CA and moved all the way across America to train and work with her in Vermont. It was one of the best years of my life in terms of growth and learning around medicine and healing. I didn't end up taking over for her since COVID-19 cut our training short and she needed to retire sooner than planned, but it ended up taking me to the third download without realizing it; writing about healing from Lyme to reach more people than just one-on-one.

3. Writing Books on Healing and Chronic Illnesses

The third image download was of a bunch of books being opened up and I saw a typewriter typing and a pen writing and more and more books ending up on a shelf. I was to write books on health and healing, specifically Lyme disease and chronic illnesses, to help reach those in need of healing support. I also saw another woman collaborating with me—she had graying hair but looked similar to the woman I saw in the first download. I got that I would be collaborating in writing some of the books at some point. I also saw that my writing and speaking would be reaching more people than I ever could working one-on-one with people. I was to put my time into the creation of the books and speaking to reach the masses around health and healing.

And so, here I am! Writing the first book of the series! I have at least eight other books, some on Lyme, others on other types of healing, and some fun ones downloaded to me and outlined to finish writing in the near future. This is the first of many, all in the purpose of reaching others and inviting them to find healing in the light as well as empowering them to take responsibility for their health in ways they can, starting today. I am on my new life path and will continue along it with pleasure and excitement!

PART I
SECTION 2

Flashback

I Worried

By Mary Oliver

I worried a lot. Will the garden grow, will the rivers
flow in the right direction, will the earth turn
as it was taught, and if not how shall
I correct it?

Was I right, was I wrong, will I be forgiven,
can I do better?

Will I ever be able to sing, even the sparrows
can do it and I am, well,
hopeless.

Is my eyesight fading or am I just imagining it,
am I going to get rheumatism,
lockjaw, dementia?

Finally I saw that worrying had come to nothing.
And gave it up. And took my old body
and went out into the morning,
and sang.

5

Tick-Toc Lyme Timeline: How It all Began

"Not I nor anyone else can travel that road for you.
You must travel it by yourself. It is not far. It is within reach.
Perhaps you have been on it since you were born and did not
know. Perhaps it is everywhere – on water and land."

-Walt Whitman

In January 2015, I left my full-time teaching job at Santa Barbara Middle School, a career I had loved and done for over fourteen years, to start my own therapy practice that focused on helping kids, teens and their families with Chronic Illness and Learning Disabilities. The stress of being a teacher with fourteen-hour days had become too hard on my health. I continued to work part-time as a trip coordinator for the middle school's outdoor education program. I thought having my own schedule in private practice and seeing fewer people in a day would help my health and well-being in the long run.

June 2015: The Bite

It was June 2015 when I got a tick bite on a mountain biking trip in Marin County. It was the last outdoor trip I would be leading for the middle school. I saw my doctor for the tick bite and received two weeks of Doxycycline. I didn't show signs of a bull's-eye rash or any flu-like symptoms. I had already been running my private practice as a marriage and family therapist (MFT) for six months with over fourteen clients a week, which was a good start. Things looked like they were all planned out and going well in my life, and it was much less stressful than teaching full-time in terms of hours of being on each day. I was excited with my new life, or so I thought.

July-August 2015: Visual Memory Loss

In July, at thirty-two years old, I got shingles in my eye and down my leg. At my age, it's rare to get shingles unless you are severely immune compromised. Also, unknown to me, my heart began to misfire with atrial fibrillation. This caused me to pass out, especially at night, most days of the week. I started having memory loss too. I continued to move forward though. I decided to take a part-time job at a cheese store in addition to my therapy practice because I thought it would be easy enough and fun. My main jobs were to make sandwiches and use the cash register. I found after one week I still could not remember the basics of either no matter how many times the owner taught me. My short-term memory was getting worse each day, and I was unable to assimilate new information, which made learning almost impossible. I remember thinking, *this is strange, what is wrong with me?*

By August, my visual memory went fully away. I first realized how bad it was while attending a Gestalt Play Therapy workshop that I had been doing once a month all year. We were assigned to draw a few things in an exercise. I went to visualize my safe space, which was always my bedroom with a tree next to it and me sitting and reading on my bed. I couldn't imagine anything. I couldn't see my room or myself. I couldn't draw anything except a stick figure of a girl and a stick figure of a tree. That was it. No matter how hard I tried, I could not retrieve the images I had always been able to see and draw from memory. The month earlier, I had drawn life-like people from memory. This was a huge wake up call, and it scared me!

The ability to draw or visualize things like maps or stick figures went away completely, which was my strongest form of memory before all this started. I was lost in a way I had never been before. Growing up with learning disabilities, including dyslexia and processing difficulties, I relied on my extremely high visual memory scores to carry me

in the areas where I was disabled. Losing my visual memory was almost equivalent to going blind in my world! My brain was declining quickly, and I was becoming a completely different person.

September-October 2015: Lost and Confused

By September and October, I was getting lost driving around Santa Barbara, where I had lived for thirty-two years and knew like the back of my hand. Most of my life I had gotten around by bicycle, so I knew all the streets, not just the main ones, inside and out. On a Tuesday morning, I loaded into my Jeep and headed out to my appointment where I had been going on Tuesdays for over ten years. But on the way there, I got really confused. It was like someone took an eraser and wiped my mind completely clean. What was happening? I tried to remember what I was doing but couldn't. It felt like my brain was going to retrieve the memory and then just fell off a cliff into an abyss to come back with nothing. An empty void, a sucking black hole, was taking everything I knew from my mind. I got off the freeway and drove a few blocks. I didn't recognize the streets any longer. I could read the signs but they meant nothing to me; "State Street". I knew it was an important main street but had no context in relation to any other place I was or had been. It went from being placed on a 2D map to floating around in my world, chaotic and making no sense. I knew it was a sign, I knew what it said, and I knew I was in Santa Barbara, whatever that meant. But I could have been anywhere in the universe. I called Adam.

"Adam, I don't know where I am."

He started to laugh. "Caroline, what do you mean you don't know where you are?" I continued, "Adam, I don't know where I am! Like, seriously, I'm staring at a sign that says *State Street* but I don't even know what that means. I don't know where I am. I'm freaking out!" Now I was starting to get a bit panicked feeling inside. Tears began to stream from my eyes but I clenched my teeth to hold them back; I don't cry. Hold it together, Caroline! And then the crying in utter confusion started without control.

"Caroline, just take a breath. Ok, I think you were on your way to the office."

"Oh yeah, the office…" My mind was completely blank. I could not see any visuals in my mind's eye of what that was supposed to mean or look like. No map popped in, showing me where I was in relation to the office.

"Where is the office? I don't know how to get there" I shouted to Adam between sobs.

"Can you look at the street corners nearest you? What do they read?"

I took a moment to breathe, and I looked around. Cars were going by people were walking and none of them were aware of how far gone I was—probably not even thinking about how strange the world can suddenly become when your brain starts to unravel. Maybe I should have named this book Unravel…

I found a sign and stammered, "*State Street...* and *Mission Street* is another."

"Ok, you are really close to your office. You just have to go down the street you are on."

"Adam, I can't do it. I don't know which way is up or down or over. None of what you say makes sense. I can't see it."

"Ok, stay where you are, just sit down in the grass. I'll come get you." And that's when Adam had to start to come get me.

Within a month, I could no longer drive myself independently without getting completely lost.

I literally couldn't figure out where I was or how to get home. One minute I knew where I was going and what I was doing, like going to the grocery store or a doctor's appointment or work, and a second later, it was like a wipe would come over me and I had no idea where I was, what I was doing, or where I had even come from to get back to. Thank God for Adam for picking up his phone and coming to my rescue again and again.

Locked Out

The other thing that started to happen daily was I would lock my keys in the car—literally every day. God Bless AAA! They knew me by first name and stopped charging me for coming out to get my keys out of my car because they felt so bad for me. They knew something wasn't right with my brain, and after seeing me crying and confused and upset as I waited for Adam to come get me each day, they just wanted to help me out. I didn't lose my ability to drive or how to operate the car in this stage, so I would drive behind Adam home and park the car there for the day, calling it quits.

November 2015: Bad Brain

In November 2015, I started to look like I might have Multiple Sclerosis and I had lots of scans that showed lesions on my brain.

While walking, my legs would completely give out with no warning, putting me face-first on the cold cement sidewalk or bathroom floor. Some days, I couldn't hold myself up or balance. Those were what I started to call my "bad brain days" and there was no real consistent correlation to know when they were coming on or not. I could still hide a lot of it in the public's eye by staying home on "bad" days and only showing up on "good" days where I still looked and acted like "Caroline" overall. Because I still had my own therapy practice, I could change my hours and make it work for my good days. I was continually assessing with the help of a therapist friend if I was hitting the line ethically where I should no longer be practicing due to my memory issues.

December 2015: The Heart of It!

In mid-December, I had to have emergency heart ablation surgery. They went up my femoral artery in my leg into my heart and burned circuits that were electrically misfiring so I wouldn't continue passing out from my heart electrically firing incorrectly through the day but especially at night. One of my best friends, Pam, invited me to come stay in her guest room where I would have a quiet week to recover after surgery. Pam was an angel to me throughout my health challenges, and also to Adam, and Alicia, my niece, who was staying with us at the time.

January 2016: Dementia

By the end of January, I could no longer drive and I had to completely shut down my therapy practice because my memory loss had turned into full-blown dementia. I'd be in the middle of a conversation with someone who I'd known for over a year as their therapist and I would suddenly have a complete memory wipe. I wouldn't know who I was or who they were mid-sentence. Ethically I could no longer push through or see clients.

At the moment when I realized it had come to the point of no longer being able to hide it, I had a complete emotional, physical, psychological, and spiritual breakdown on all levels with the reality of how serious my health issues had become. I couldn't make it to work anymore after I had worked so hard, going to school and getting my license as an LMFT, to get to the place I was at as a therapist on my own. I was devastated and confused and scared. I had lost all hope and it only grew worse.

February-March 2016: Changes in Perception
Loss of Color Vision

In the first week of March 2016, I was in a therapy session when suddenly the entire room including my therapist turned into a black-and-white film, with the color blue added. All I could see were grays and blues. All other color had disappeared. Completely.

One minute I was talking about something that was challenging me with my health and the next my sight completely changed to only grays and blues. He was blown away when I told him and I started asking him what color he saw things as. "What color is your desk right now?" I would ask, and he would say brown with black lines. I would say "To me it's a light shade of gray and the outer edge is blue." The sky was bright blue with grayscale trees and cars on the street his office overlooked. This continued for the next week. I went straight to my neurologist from his office but I was told the usual; "There is nothing I can do for you since your scans all look normal. It's probably just in your head. You may want to see a psychologist."

"I literally was just with my psychologist and he sent me to you. This *is* in my head; it's something happening inside my physical brain. I need your help."

"Like I told you, there is nothing I can do. You don't fit any of the criteria I have been trained in. There is nothing I can do."

Dumbfounded, I walked out of his office and went to find another neurologist, *again*. This would be number three. So you know, my scans did show problems, many lesions throughout my brain, but he didn't know what to do with them.

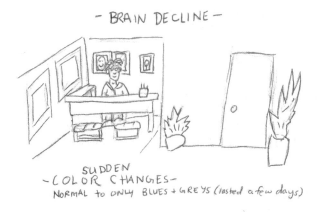

— BRAIN DECLINE —

SUDDEN
— COLOR CHANGES —
NORMAL to ONLY BLUES + GREYS (lasted a few days)

The Matrix is real?!

The other thing that came with my change in color vision was that I started to be able to see more grid-like lines and wave patterns emanating from birds, trees, and buildings when I was out walking in the world. I could sit and stare at things for hours because they were so fascinating. A tree had so many layers of waves and frequencies coming off it and it was so similar to the other things around it, just slightly different in waves, and I could see it. Something was changing inside my brain physically and chemically. I wasn't crazy, it was really happening.

These experiences all taught me through experience how we are all energy, we are all light, and we can heal in more ways than one. Perception is not reality. The possibilities are endless. Science is not certain or always explainable. There is so much more to us than just the physical. Matter makes up the physical but matter itself is made up of waves of energy and space. Lots of space between—mostly empty—yet we seem solid! There is so much we don't know and so there is always hope to get better, to heal, and to overcome any illness or diagnosis. The possibilities are way more available than most western medicine wants you to believe. Science has become a religion in itself in some ways, limiting our abilities to heal in ways that can't always be explained. This is why prayer and intentions can physically change us and heal us too. We are all connected to the source, the universe, God, and we have the ability to shift our frequency into another one if we ask for help, have faith, and set our intention to be healed.

Grid Pictures ↗
↓

• Everything was energy + had different frequencies.
• Like a grid with waves of frequencies

"There is always hope to get better."

The next week, I was seeing a new neurologist who ordered a spinal tap to assess pressure and infections in my spinal fluid. He also ordered MRIs of my spine and brain again. The scans showed I had lesions all over my brain and in my spine. He ran a few memory tests in his office and ordered me to get a neuropsychological evaluation that ended up showing cognitive decline and dementia. In a month's time, he had gathered all the info he needed to diagnose me.

"You have early onset dementia. It looks to be rapid onset. There isn't much we can do. There really isn't any treatment."

Zombie Movie- The Final March- The Last Hurrah!

In March 2016, Alicia had spring break, and Adam and I took Alicia and a friend of hers, Osiris, on a week-long camping trip to Avila Hot Springs and Hearst Castle in California. I was along for the ride, living all in the moment from the passenger seat, literally and figuratively. On the trip, Alicia and Osiris made a zombie movie starring me as the main zombie who ate brains all day. I share this only because it is sort of eerie to go back and watch the video now, seeing myself as a literal brain zombie—a fictional one in the movie, but I was literally a walking zombie in my daily life, and I get why they chose me as that.

Only two weeks after returning from that trip and making that movie, I would have a stroke and a near death experience that I could not foresee coming. It's a bit eerie to watch the movie knowing what was coming next in real life.

-ZOMBIE LAND-
FILM

April 2016: Stroke of NeuroLyme

April 15th, 2016: Stroke!

April 17, 2016: Near Death

April 25th, 2016: Testing confirms Neurological Lyme Disease plus 13 co-infections. Begin Lyme Treatment!

Looking Back, I Never Gave Up Hope That My Brain Would Heal

Throughout the time I was losing my memory I continued to read and research all that I could to try to figure out what was causing my brain and body to fail. I just kept telling myself to trust that what I was trying to learn and read was going in and getting stored somewhere in my brain so one day I would be able to get back to retrieve it even though I couldn't now. I also figured it couldn't hurt to read and exercise my brain even if I couldn't remember—maybe one day I'd find the key and then all this information would be accessible when I was better. And guess what? It was! Three years later, it's strange that now as my brain continues to heal itself, I am actually getting some of my memories back from that lost year that I didn't even know were recorded. So they were encoded throughout my time without memory even though I couldn't retrieve them. Now I'm in a space where the linear timeline is synching with the memories during the time I had dementia and memory formation is coming back and getting stronger. It just shows how the brain and body are amazing at healing!! You are never too old to heal and make new neural connections! Neuroplasticity is much broader than what neuroscientists used to think. Stay positive, visualize, and pray for your body and mind to heal fully, and they can!

"Where there's hope, there's life.
It fills us with fresh courage and makes us strong again."

-Anne Frank, The Diary of a Young Girl

There was relief for me when I hit the state of being in the moment, which meant dementia. But it was very hard on those who loved me watching me deteriorate and not be able to function on my own or remember what we had just done together. I have so much empathy and compassion for family members who have a loved one with any type of memory loss and or chronic illness, and I am so thankful for Adam and Alicia who had to watch me deteriorate, unable to do anything to stop me from getting worse. And yet they stayed by my side and helped me every day, loving me just the same.

6

Memory Loss:
Living in the Moment

*"Happiness, not in another place but this place...
not for another hour, but this hour."*

-Walt Whitman

Grocery Shopping

It's a Saturday afternoon. Alicia and I are at the grocery store shopping together getting the groceries for the week.

"Cheese, we need cheese." I say to Alicia. "I will get the cheese."

And I take off into the store. Alicia goes and gets other items on our list. We find each other near the front of the store.

She asks, "Care, did you get the cheese?" I stare blankly at her, knowing I was supposed to remember what "getting the cheese" meant, but I honestly didn't.

"What cheese?"

Alicia smiles at me and laughs, "Care, you were going to get the cheese."

"I was?" I asked, laughing. "Ok, don't worry I'll get the cheese!" I take off towards the cheese but on the way I see essential oils and think "Oh, I need some of those." The next thing you know, I am in the moment and all else has escaped me. Out of habit and muscle memory, I head back to the front of the store with lavender and rosemary oils in my hand.

Again, Alicia looks at me in the check-out line. She's smiling at me. "Did you get the cheese?"

"What cheese?"

Silence. She starts laughing.

We are both laughing now. But in all reality, this is how everyday had become. I was just where I was, when I was. In each moment. To remember for two aisles what food item I was to get was too much for my short-term memory. Thank God for my niece and husband, otherwise I would have probably starved to death! Literally.

In the Moment

I was living completely in the moment, moment to moment. And in that state of dementia, as crazy as it sounds, there was a huge gift of experience. I no longer had the emotions of shame, guilt, or fear. All of these emotions rely on a sense of time, which I now lacked without memory.

It was terrible for those around me watching me go through it, though. They thought they were losing me, that I was dying before their eyes, and that I wasn't sane. The truth is in a weird way I was more sane and more real than ever before. I was out of society's loops and training, and I couldn't understand why people (or myself) even put that extra energy out all the time to fix and hide shame, which wasn't even real in the first place.

Shame lives in the past, fear lives in the future, and I lived in the now-present moment when I had full-blown dementia.

Shameless

So as my health and brain deteriorated, the emotion of shame disappeared as well—no memory of past events allowed me to be free of feeling embarrassed or shamed about anything I had done (or just did). I was free from worrying about what others thought of me. This caused me to speak very directly, and sometimes too bluntly, but I was in such a space of "now" I wasn't meaning anything I said as judgmental or bad—I was stating it just as it was in that moment. I didn't know I needed to sugarcoat or not say something because I didn't have shame or feel it for other people to predict what would happen if I said something wrong. I was free!

I realized how many hours we spend a day worried about what others are thinking about us. We waste so much of our time and energy on outside, uncontrollable things, and it's a great distraction from being who we are and being happy with what we are doing in the moment. This was a huge gift from losing my memory and it healed so many of those core beliefs that shaped me and I had worked on in therapy for years. But now they were just gone because my past was gone and not attached to me in the now any longer!

Memory Loss

Losing your memory is like a reset button. A re-birthing process. As babies and little children, we come into this world fresh and new with no programming around what is right or wrong. Our past hasn't imprinted shame into us by telling us we are internally flawed.

This toxic shame that we all have in some form inside us by adulthood is just that—toxic. It creates toxins in your physical body and energy field. It stirs things up and makes you vibrate at a frequency that invites physical things in at the same frequency—not good or bad, just the same frequency, so shame is a lower frequency emotional state.

"I want to believe that the imperfections are nothing—
that the light is everything."

- Mary Oliver

Shame and Guilt

Shame relies on remembering something from your past like what you said or did that made you feel embarrassed or bad in some way. When shame is activated, I call it being put in a shame trance state. It's when you beat yourself up inside, and you want to hide from everyone and everything. It is the most awful feeling in your stomach and body that makes you sick. Being "shy" usually comes from having some internal shame or core belief that there is something internally wrong with you from something that happened when you were a kid—"I'm stupid", "I'm ugly", "I'm bad", "I'm unlovable", or "I'm unworthy".

Guilt relies on the past as well, and on a memory of doing something you shouldn't have, a bad act in some way. But you aren't internally bad because of it; it was just a bad choice or action that you knew you shouldn't have done. You did a bad action but it doesn't mean you are a *bad* person. Guilt is "I did something bad, like stole cookies from the cookie jar when I knew I shouldn't and I feel guilty about it." Guilt is there to help guide us on making ethically kind decisions and live together in society in peace. Shame is when you feel "**I am** bad. I am bad all the time at a core level." This is where it becomes a toxic program that stops serving us at a soul level for our growth.

Fear

While shame and guilt come from our past, fear lives in MAKING UP STORIES ABOUT **being aware of** our future and wanting to control it. Fear relies on a combo of the past and the future because it lives there—what if this happens? What if . . .? It relies on us projecting and predicting what is coming by pulling from our past experiences and knowledge, making these predictions and "what if's", and not being able to control the future and getting scared and anxious about that.

Lightning Strike

A huge gift that came from losing my memory I found was losing the feeling of fear overall in my life. I remember the exact moment this happened for me. I was in the car with Adam. We got off the freeway for our house. It was a stormy, rainy day and a bolt of lightning hit in the distance with a loud boom of thunder following instantly after it, cracking my eardrums. I felt no fear.

Now you need to know one thing about me: my number one fear for my entire life up to this point had always been being struck by lightning because a lot of my family members have been hit. As early as I could remember, I would go into a complete panic if lightning was around. I would shake, freeze, and cry. My parents would have to take me into the car and tell me it was safe because of the tires on a car, even in the middle of the night. I never outgrew it. Riding my bike across America in the Midwest, we met up with lightning daily and I would tremble in terror for the hour it was around, hiding where I could. Today something was different. Way different.

As we started to roll through the intersection to head home from the freeway, the lightning bolt hit. What did I do? I saw it and instantly turned and said to Adam, "Take me to it! I want to get as close as I can to the lightning strike! Can we find it! It's beautiful!" He looked at me in total shock and said, "Caroline, you're scared to death of lightning."

"I am?" I said. "Just start driving towards it, I want to find it!" He said, "No Caroline that's crazy, it's not safe." And I remember now, with my memories back, wanting so badly to be right in the lightning storm, feeling the electricity of it all and seeking it out! That was the moment I lost my memory of fear or the ability to feel fear overall. All anxiety about the future was gone. I was just in the now and in the now there is no future. Nothing to fear because you just are.

· LOSS OF FEAR ·

Lightning became a very important symbol to me in my healing after that. In nature, it is a catalyst. To me, it was a catalyst of change, and when I came back into my body after the near-death, I knew I was to be a catalyst for others to find their healing abilities on their healing journey.

I suddenly had no memory of future plans, schedules, goals, and dreams (which are all good things for motivation in real life). In not having access to these memories of what was to come or what had happened in the past, suddenly all anxiety, worry, shame, stress, and fear were gone. It was peaceful to say the least for me. But very scary for my partner to watch.

Fear disappeared.
No memory of future plans or events made the worry of what could be go away.

It was stressful and concerning for my family and friends who still had their memory of future and past intact and were able to look ahead to my future and imagine all the ways my future was looking shorter and bleaker than ever before. So I am sorry for all the stress I put my loved ones through. I was less stressed than them even with being so sick because I couldn't remember how sick I was at this point.

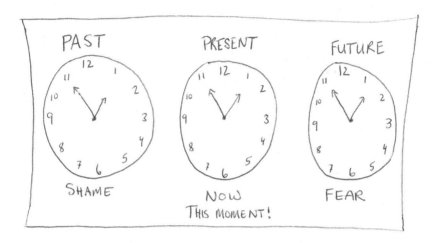

But the huge gift was this: when you completely lose your memory or ability to construct time outside of this moment, you lose these three toxic emotional states completely. This doesn't happen in the beginning of memory loss, but when you truly have hit the dementia stage, which I did, where no short-term memory really existed anymore, I was free of some very heavy emotions like anxiety and fear and shame that as humans we all have weighing us down in ways we are not aware of. They stop us from living in the present moment and with joy. The gift was I got to experience what it actually felt to live in the "now" without having to fight all those human emotions that get in the way.

Once I got past the confusion, frustration, and awareness of the memory loss stage, I wasn't happy, but I wasn't upset any longer either. I was neutral. Life just "was." I just was.

"For how many years have you gone through the house, shutting the windows, while the rain was still five miles away."

- Mary Oliver

7

Surprising Gifts of an Unraveling Brain

"Every hour of every day is an unspeakably perfect miracle."

-Walt Whitman

A gift I received from these experiences with having neurological Lyme disease was the ability to see how intention and our emotions can make a situation better or worse. Once I could no longer work or drive, I created purpose and routine in my daily life by taking my dog to the Douglas Family Preserve overlooking the ocean to sit on the ground and try to write or just be. What I learned about energy and our world, due to my unraveling brain and state of consciousness, was eye opening about the power of intention, words, and thoughts on the energy body. This directly affects the physical body and our behaviors. We affect all of those around us by either adding to the world in a positive way or a negative way. We can choose our behaviors, thoughts, and emotions, and shift our breathing, to change others and our own bodies. It's that simple. Let me share some of the days my unraveling brain taught me this.

Once I stopped being able to work or drive on my own, I still needed something to do during the day to give me a sense of purpose. To ensure I couldn't get lost, I found a short trail that did one loop along a bluff overlooking the ocean in the Douglas Family Preserve property. My job was to take Lilli, our big fluffy labradoodle, for a walk each day. I found an amazing fallen tree in the meadow where I was walking and decided it would be the spot where I would go each day and hang out because there was something about the earth's energy that I could feel when sitting there.

It was now February and it had been a month since I had stopped working for the first time since I was 11 years old. I always had a job growing up. I loved having purpose and work where I could help people with something and make some money so I could buy the things I needed, like underwear or food. So to not be off doing even some type of part-time job was very confusing to me and causing a lot of inner stress about my identity and purpose for being alive. I was being forced to learn to surrender, to slow down, to be still and let others take care of me, which was completely against my normal role in my life. I had learned to make the world safe by becoming in control through taking care of things, taking care of others, and having enough money to always take care of myself—all these coping mechanisms were being pulled from my grasp, literally from moment to moment, and getting worse.

One day, Adam came to pick me up from the Douglas Family Preserve like we had designated on my schedule for that week. He found me sitting on a rock at the front gate to the trail. He gave me a hug and started walking me to his car. I suddenly stopped and just started crying. (You have to understand I gave up crying as a young kid. I learned to laugh and not cry because it didn't help me in my family system and I became more vulnerable than was safe emotionally). So crying was a big deal. He asked me if I was alright.

I started screaming at him. "Am I alright? How can you ask that! I'm anything but alright. I am a burden to you, I am a burden to society, I can't contribute anything to anyone. I wish I could just die because I have nothing to give and I am just taking up precious resources staying alive!" I was sobbing now and walking. I didn't want to be held or comforted. Adam stared at me, dumbfounded, since this was so the opposite of who I normally was: the optimistic, creative thinker who helped everyone get out of their despair and confusion, but now it was my turn.

He started telling me he loved me and that I did have purpose and that I wasn't a burden. I couldn't hear it. I wanted to die. I wanted to end the downward spiral. I truly felt like *all* purpose was gone so I was just wasting his energy and time and money by being alive. I hated myself! I hated the situation and that no doctor could figure out what was causing it. I couldn't remember anything long enough to figure it out myself like I was accustomed to doing. This all happened a few weeks before I lost fear and shame from my experiences, which I talk about in a future chapter.

This was another stage in the complete unraveling. Adam finally caught me and held me in his arms as I cried. I tried to wiggle free but there was no hope with his big bear arms around me. I calmed down enough to agree to get into the car, but the feeling of being a complete burden on everyone around me, the earth included resource-wise, did not leave for the rest of the day. Good news is once I went to sleep, it all reset, and I forgot all about it in the morning when I awoke. It was like I had a wipe clean each time I slept. LOL.

"I may not have gone where I intended to go, but I think I have ended up where I needed to be."

- Douglas Adams

The Douglas Preserve became my work and purpose. I was to walk the dog there, sit, meditate, journal, or rest on the earth. I brought a few big blankets in a backpack to lay on, a journal, pen, my cell phone, water, and a snack each day. Something amazing started happening later in February.

Waves of Energy

Another gift from the unraveling of my brain came to me. I began to see energy waves all around me. It was like reality, as I knew it, started to alter or lose its ability to look whole and normal. I was having glitches in my perception. I would literally see matter as a grid made out of waves of energy that were just vibrating at different speeds, and that was the only thing making them into different material things.

A stick had a different frequency wave as matter than the dirt I lay on or the backpack I carried. People all had different energy waves coming off them and, over time, I even started seeing colors and shades around them in their fields.

Another stage in my brain's normal abilities unraveling had brought me another gift, in a way. The world became so beautiful, and I would spend hours sitting on my blankets absorbing the waves of energy coming off the earth. It was fantastic! I wonder if it was similar to what those who do psychedelics experience? I would not know because I have never done any mind-altering drugs before. I became very aware of the earth's frequency and how its waves were healing to our bodies because I could see and feel the energy exchange.

I wrote about how I could tell I could heal if I could get more of the frequency of the earth into me. That is what I was missing and needing. I became physically stronger during my time at the preserve.

I journaled about my experiences too. I felt like I was being shown something that I would be able to share with others in the future, and my fear of not having purpose began to dissipate because I could see I had hope. I had purpose to get better and help others wake up to the reality that they are energy too and, to heal physical illness, you must also heal your energy field if you want to get better fully.

I started to see my brain *unraveling* as a new classroom—and the universe and nature were my teachers. I didn't know what I would be shown next, so each day became exciting again. I just kept writing down everything I was experiencing since I couldn't remember anything longer than a few minutes at this point. But I was trusting it was going in somewhere, and it was. I have all the memories of what happened now, six years later, and if any are still missing, they are coming back in chunks randomly as time goes on, these little surprising gifts from above as I heal.

Dog Fight

Here is an entry from my journal that I wrote on one of my visits to the Douglas Family Preserve with Lilli, my labradoodle. I share this because I feel that I learned a very big lesson about how much my reactions, emotions, and breath affect me and others. This is huge for the potential you have on your own ability to heal. I was so thankful to be given these gifts on some of my darkest days of unraveling.

February 2016

Dear Journal,

So today I woke up later and read a book, relaxed. Adam came over and we cuddled for half an hour which is really nice. I was feeling a little better than yesterday. And I packed things up to go over to the Douglas Family Preserve property with Lilli to spend a couple hours sitting and doing meditation towards my healing. I was excited about the weather and the rain coming because I like to be in rain outside when it's warm.

I got there and I got really comfortable and was laying down on my special spot with Lily lying next to me. I connected quickly into the God energy-type trance state and was feeling really relaxed and full and good inside. I started seeing and hearing more insights and putting things together . . . I had totally relaxed and melted into the earth again and was really enjoying it. I was about to get a notepad out when a giant pit bull came bouncing through the bush behind us and surprised Lilli, who jumped up and growled a little but then started wagging her tail and was fine from being startled. I jumped up and then the pit bull's owner was yelling for it to come back, and then it got scared and weird. It looked scared to me and it suddenly came at Lilli and attacked her and locked it's jaws on her neck. Lilli began to cry.

The owner and I tried to get her dog to release its jaw and nothing was working. A big guy came to help us, who was walking nearby, and nothing he did helped, and everyone was screaming and hitting the dog and picking it up and prying its jaw, but it was locked onto Lilli's neck. I was in such a deep meditative trance when this all started and I was taking sound and smells in so strongly and seeing energy waves. I stepped back a few feet and looked at the dogs and people trying to get them to separate, but I could only hear and sense the dog attacking for some reason. It was like God wanted my attention to focus in on the attacking dog only. I could smell and see how scared both Lilli and this pit bull were—the attacking dog was so frightened, and its jaw was genetically bred to kill and do this when in fear. I could see it and sense it and smell the fear—it couldn't let go if it wanted to while in this level of fear.

I could smell its pheromones separate from Lilli's which I can smell from across our house if something's wrong. I yelled to everyone, people and dogs, "Stop! Everyone calm down. Stop! We have to be calm." The two people looked shocked to hear me saying stop when my dog was in the grip of the other dog's jaw, dying.

"Everyone take a deep breath in, NOW, on the count of three—one, two, three . . ." And everyone looked at me and I breathed in and they breathed in, and we breathed out all together in unison, and the pit bull immediately relaxed and its jaw released off Lilli's neck and its tail went between its legs and it ran to its owner, scared, to hide behind her. Lilli ran to me crying, and both the other owner and I collapsed to the ground with our dogs in our arms and in total shock.

The man who stopped to help walked off a bit perplexed at how that worked . . . but it was done.

I wasn't angry or mad at all. The pit bull was just as scared as Lilli and it didn't want to be locked to her—it couldn't release its jaw and it was getting hit and kicked and yanked and pushed. I saw in its eyes it was terrified and stuck, and when I realized we all needed to breathe and slow down, it allowed the pit bull's brain to turn the switch back off from fear to safety. She looked relieved to be able to release her jaw and so scared and confused about what had just happened.

I wasn't angry, which was weird. I think because I was in such a calm state from the unraveling of my brain and being in meditation with collective consciousness, source, and God right before it happened. It was an accident. The owner of the other dog was in the exact same shock and upset as me. Exhausted and bruised and upset, we sat on the earth for a few minutes, catching our breath and calming our dogs and looking at each other in shock and disbelief.

This was different for me—usually I would get big and loud from fear and surprise like this. I'd blame the owner or dog for being bad or out of control. Instead, I saw her and her dog equal to Lilli and me. We all had the same traumatic experience. Lilli may have been the victim in the attack, but we were all suffering from trauma from the event and needed love and care for healing, not anger.

I am still in shock some I think because I don't feel a lot yet other than the fear that poor pit bull was feeling and the pain Lilli was feeling. Those are the two things I do feel probably because of my brain being off and taking in heightened senses of smell and sound in without filtering has made me more intuitive. I am able to read animals' feelings and sense their fear or joy or pheromones. It makes it hard for me to get angry at a dog who was so scared at the same time she was being aggressive.

The dog didn't have any control and was frightened, and Lilli was hurting, and I couldn't do anything to help her for a few minutes until I realized we, humans, trying to separate the dogs, were all acting as bad as the dog attacking—aggressively kicking and hitting and pulling at the pit bull to get her off Lilli. I could see now in the form of energy waves we were just adding more of the same aggressive vibration and anger that the pit bull had. The pit bull wasn't going to release or stop with that tone and energy being added to her frenzied state. We were in essence adding fear and anger energy to the fire of fear that was already there in the pit bull's and Lilli's energy fields, and this was why the pit bull's jaw was locked on to Lilli's neck.

So that's when it clicked for me: we all needed to shift our energy and tone to calmness and safety. I told everyone to stop and calm down and take a breath together and it worked. It was like hitting the release button on a switch. Instantly the dogs relaxed and the pit bull was able to release its locked jaw off of Lilli's neck.

Everything stopped.

From this terrible experience in terms of Lilli being hurt pretty badly, she had to have three surgeries, lots of stitches and drains . . . The good thing that came from it was the message I received through my experience of being more open from the meditation and brain unraveling. I would have never been able to sense or see if I had been 100% healthy still doing my type-A living style.

I learned that if I dwell on negative stuff, complain, think bad thoughts about someone or something—I'm just adding and joining vibrationally to that thing I don't want. I'm choosing to be in the thing I don't want energy-wise. It was in my control more than I realized and pretty simple as a concept. Like attracts like, and adding more of the same thing only makes it bigger. If you don't like how you feel, you can always choose to use tools to shift your energy to one of a higher vibration just by putting yourself around those emotions and experiences and words and thoughts. Eventually, you will start to shift into a better state.

Some say fight fire with fire, that just makes a bigger fire. We all took a breath and paused, and out went the fire! When we cooled it with its opposite frequency— peace, stillness, and calmness—became our water.

You can always do something to help yourself heal. Meditating or praying are ways to shift your vibration to one of light and healing. Asking for help, finding gratitude in anything you can near you, changing your posture to be more upright and looking up release chemicals of optimism even when you feel down. You can use your smile muscles even if you don't feel happy and it actually will grow and become a real smile. The muscles in a smile activate and strengthen our thymus gland to be healthier and grow in size, which is a good thing.

These small things can shift us out of our funks and into states of wellness. It can be hard to motivate to do it when we are in our deepest slumps, though, so don't beat yourself up if you just need to go through a slump sometimes. Just know you always have some choice and tools to get yourself moving out of them when you are ready—and they work. I am so thankful for these everyday wonders and for my health challenges and unraveling which gave me the tools to change my life for the positive.

Then I realized that this is what people, myself included, do a lot. They focus on what they don't want or on stop-

ping something instead of on what they need or want. We wanted the dogs to be peaceful but we put off very different frequency energy and vibration just with our breath. I now can see how much our breath shows our frequency at any given time... It shows our emotional state and our health. The dogs taught me this.

Once I realized we were part of the problem and that we all actually really did control the dogs—not by what we said or told them to do, or physically tried to do to them, but with our breath. It was that simple. It was with our vibration and our emotion and expectation we put out to the world through our breath. Dogs follow our unannounced thoughts a lot of the time. They read this energy and vibration and our smells (pheromones). Now that my brain is off and turned on in this way, my ability to read animals is completely different. I feel what they feel without trying. It's so distracting if I need to be doing adult stuff, but when relaxed in nature, it's better this way.

My brain not being able to filter sounds and touch and smells is what is causing it. I think this is why autistic kids I have worked with have always loved dogs and animals overall. They can read them more than most humans from the heightened senses coming in unfiltered.

Anyway, Lilli is home curled up in a soft crate on my bed with Adam. She has tubes draining from her and lots of meds. I hurt so much hearing her crying and seeing her wounds, but I'm thankful for her being okay and the huge message she taught me during the fight for my life . . .

We all have choice, no matter how bad our lives become, to shift our thoughts but more importantly our breath, and the rate and depth of the breath is huge in shifting our vibration. The spirit is directly connected to our breath and so it makes sense it is powerful and a key part of our commu-

nicating with one another in non-verbal communication. Signing off, going to bed! I'm exhausted.

Caroline

-End of Journal entry 2016-

PART I

SECTION 3

Post Stroke and Near Death
Healing Journey

The Fourth Sign of the Zodiac (Part 3)

By Mary Oliver

I know, you never intended to be in this world.
But you're in it all the same.

So why not get started immediately.

I mean, belonging to it.
There is so much to admire, to weep over.

And to write music or poems about.

Bless the feet that take you to and fro.
Bless the eyes and the listening ears.
Bless the tongue, the marvel of taste.
Bless touching.

You could live a hundred years, it's happened.
Or not.
I am speaking from the fortunate platform
of many years,
none of which, I think, I ever wasted.
Do you need a prod?
Do you need a little darkness to get you going?
Let me be as urgent as a knife, then,
and remind you of Keats,
so single of purpose and thinking, for a while,
he had a lifetime.

8

Road to Recovery

"The powerful play goes on and you may contribute a verse."

-Walt Whitman

Once I was discharged from the hospital, I began a long road to recovery and healing from the stroke and began the process of diagnosing what caused it. Early onset dementia was not the cause, and that diagnosis was removed from my labels. A doctor in the hospital whispered to Adam and me that I should get tested for Lyme disease since I worked as an outdoor trip leader with kids, but he would not order the testing himself or write it in my chart because he would get in trouble with the hospital. It is so interesting to see how scared Allopathic doctors are of diagnosing or even speaking about Lyme disease. And guess what, he was right!

The day I left the hospital, I called my doctor to order the right tests, and we had a mobile phlebotomist named Liz come to our home and draw my blood to test for Lyme and co-infections of all sorts. I came back positive for multiple species of Borrelia and co-infections for Lyme disease. I had neurological Lyme disease, Bartonella, Babesia, Tick-borne Relapsing Fever, Rickettsia, Ehrlichia, Anaplasma, C. Pneumonia, multiple viral infections, and many parasites showing positive a week later. I began multiple antibiotics, antivirals, and supplements for treatment, and I got my memory back almost instantly—not all at once, but it began to noticeably come back.

The die-off from treatment was horrendous. I felt like I was going to die again multiple times. I ended up in the ER five times and I had to go very slow with lots of detoxification support in place to survive the treatments in the first few months. It is so important to work with a Lyme-trained specialist while treating for this reason. The biotoxins that are released as you kill these infections can make you very ill and can become dangerous, even life-threatening, if too much is released too fast. You need a doctor who knows how to treat slow and steady, supporting your body's systems with supplements and guided activities like baths, enemas, saunas, walking, and massage while supporting your hormones and balancing malnutrition issues.

The Gift of Rewiring My Nervous System

I also realized that, when I came back into my body in the MRI machine from the near death experience with a reset nervous system, the wiring for my past triggers—post-traumatic-stress from years of very stressful childhood—was not active anymore automatically. I realized that if I kept away from a lot of people and the world in general for the first few months after my near-death reset, I could prevent the rewiring of those old and very worn trigger tracks in my nervous system. In 1949, Donald Hebb famously said, "Neurons that fire together, wire together." He was a neuropsychologist and described how pathways in the brain are formed and reinforced through repetition. I figured if I could prevent my neurons from firing on these trigger pathways by avoiding people for a few months, maybe they would sort of die away. Guess what? They did!

How did I isolate myself in a very crowded world living in southern California? I put myself in a room in my husband's office downtown for three months after the stroke to recover away from all my old routines and people who I would more likely get "old triggers" firing around. I let my body, my spirit, and my nervous system take in the reset fully and consciously. I only chose to allow in positive music, positive movies, and positive people. No stressors.

Reinhabiting My Body

I focused on exercises to rehab my physical body, like swimming and walking, which forced cross-wiring for the brain since they require moving both sides of your body in what is called a cross-lateral movement. When I began swimming, the right side of my body was extremely weak and unbalanced compared to my left. Walking was the same. I swam and walked until I could do it evenly and both sides were balanced. It took over two years to get there, but I just kept doing it every day. I'd start out extremely short and work up to thirty minutes to an hour a day and became more and more balanced.

I had very little control or strength on my right side after the stroke, so it took the full three months to even be at a spot where I could use the right side without support. I listened to hypnosis healing audio recordings that my hypnotherapist made for me. We would focus on what areas I wanted to heal each week and I would listen to it many times throughout the week. I would lay in the grass to ground my body and stay on the earth. I had this constant feeling like at any moment I could just float away off Earth again and on to the other side. I felt vulnerable and how close I came to death for months after the near-death.

I was also focused on treating and taking all the right meds and supplements, as well as doing the supportive detoxifying activities I could from my own home that I talk about in Part III of this book. At times I would think, *Geez, I am not doing anything, and I am disabled. I should be doing more and working.* But looking back on it, treatment and healing was a complete full-time job and it took all day just to stay alive and get my life back to wellness. So always remind yourself that you *are* working and you *are* being very productive if you are working on healing yourself and doing the supportive activities. You also have to focus on the psychological and emotional challenges of having Lyme, which involves cleaning up your communication and contracts with friends and family and rebuilding yourself and life from the ground up! It's a full-time job and, without your health, you have nothing! You can't do anything if you aren't alive, so enjoy your time healing and own it. Know that it is only "a moment" in your long, extraordinary life journey. A moment that will pass like all the others. That is one thing we know: time keeps moving forward while on Earth even if we wish it wouldn't sometimes.

"What is it you plan to do with your one wild and precious life?"

-Mary Oliver

You Can Heal

I was told by all my doctors, at different times and each on their own accord, that they were completely perplexed and in awe of how fast I was healing and that they didn't know how I was doing it. It was a miracle. My Lyme specialist told me three months after the stroke that he had thought he would never see me again because I would be dead, and he really felt like he had failed me. He told me he had many patients that were in better spots then me and had died shortly after. He was in tears when I walked into his office three months later for a follow-up—healthier, stronger, able to walk, and use my brain again.

The woman who was doing my bioenergetic testing was blown away when she started scanning me three months after giving me the news I had so many infections, which were all confirmed by blood testing after seeing her. She was scanning me and kept saying she couldn't believe it, the infections were so much lower or gone. What had I done? She had never seen someone heal so fast who was in such bad shape. Miraculous! She even thought her scanner wasn't working and started again. But it was getting an accurate read on me.

I had listened to my higher self and followed my knowing from the near-death that if I stayed in a frequency of love and light, I would heal quickly. The hypnosis recordings I had made with my therapist were crucial in keeping my mind positive and on track. Also, if you are mentally and emotionally well the physical treatments like meds and supplements work better, and I was able to recover from die-off reactions and the high toxic burden faster.

Strikes of Insight: Rewiring Brain

My memory came back in chunks out of nowhere a lot of the time. It would almost feel like a lightning bolt jolt or electricity when my brain would suddenly rewire or get access to something missing. I didn't know it was missing since the beauty of being the one losing your memory is that you don't know that you have lost anything! It's just gone. But when it would come back, it always blew me away, like, "Oh, wow, I didn't even know I was missing that important information." And it almost tickled my brain and I laughed.

I remember distinctly getting back my visual memory for the first chunk—it was being able to see a map of the city of Santa Barbara in my head to drive somewhere I needed to go. It was like a whole new world opened up. I could visualize where I was and where I needed to go without reading directions as words on a piece of paper. That happened about three years after the stroke. Until then I had to use written word instructions to get anywhere in my once-familiar hometown, otherwise I would get lost.

Rewriting Contracts: Social and Emotional Body Reconstruction

While staying in the office for the first few months of healing after the stroke, I made appointments with friends and family I considered to be in my inner circle. My first task to complete was rewriting contracts with those in my life. I could only handle seeing one person a day and usually only three people total in a week, so I scheduled lunch meetings with them and actually spoke about spiritual and physical contracts we hold with each other. I looked at whether each person was energetically and emotionally and physically balanced. If I felt after the lunch meeting that they were not open to changing the imbalances and wanted to stay the same—if it wasn't equal in "energy in-energy out"—then I would decide to let them go. I would still love them, but I was going to need to re-write our spiritual contract and have really good boundaries with them in terms of getting together. I could not have any relationships that would be draining energetically due to imbalances. It was no longer healthy for me. I could now see and feel that this is what lead to parasites and health issues and stress.

When I was ready to move home with our housemates, I had to have very clear boundaries on my space and energy. This caused some conflict at first since I was changing my rules and seemed like I was being mean. But in the long run, it was healthier for all of us because it gave my housemates permission to have their own boundaries and limits and communicate them with me. Win-win in the long run for all of us and we became closer because of it.

Reintegrating Daily Life Purpose and Routine

I continued to do my many health support treatments at home each day—enemas, walking, lymphatic massage, taking saunas, ozone therapy, etc. About nine months into treatment, I was starting to feel a pull for having a bit more purpose or routine in my life since I was always used to working careers that were from early morning to late evening.

A friend of mine got a puppy and asked me if I would come to his house and dog sit during the day so he could go to work. That way, the puppy would have someone to watch her and help train her to be a good dog. All I had to do was come over and hang out on his couch with the dog for the day and, if I felt up for walking her, I could take her out to do things. So I now had a schedule each day. I would get up to drive or be dropped off at his house with the dog in the morning and my husband would pick me up in the afternoon to go home. I had purpose—a simple purpose and a simple schedule to start having a routine.

"Because of the dog's joyfulness, our own is increased.
It is no small gift."

- Mary Oliver

This was the first step in my starting to see how much having purpose helps people heal more quickly. It gives you hope and meaning, especially when you hit challenging days and moments in your treatment. That puppy took care of me on some of my hardest Herxing die-off days. She just curled up with me and slept as I felt sick from Herxing on the couch, feeling horrible. I continued to treat and take care of the dog for the next two years. It was great.

I started getting asked by more and more people I met over the four years following the stroke and neurological Lyme diagnosis if I would help them heal from Lyme as well. A lot of the information in the book series I am working on covers the topics people asked me for help with, which is why I decided to write these books.

About three years into my healing, I knew I wanted to work in the medicine and healing field in some way. I was most drawn to the bioenergetic testing that I was receiving for my treatments and wanted to work with the woman who did that. I knew in my gut it was what I was supposed to be doing next. A month later, without me reaching out to her, she called me up one morning and asked if I would like to come train with her. She said she hoped I would take over her business in the future. I was beside myself! Of course I wanted to do it! Yes! And I had tested negative for Lyme disease finally a few months earlier, so I was in remission and clear health-wise to start looking at rewriting my career and purpose in life. A few months later, I was flying to Vermont to live and train with her for a year. It was great. I saw this as the end of my main healing journey with Lyme disease and the start of my new life.

I was so blessed for everything I experienced, even the bad stuff, because it taught me so much spiritually, emotionally, physically, and socially that I can now share with others to help find their light in the dark times. I didn't end up taking over her business with COVID-19 starting up and her need to retire too soon, but we stayed friends and are working as co-authors on a future book on healing. We will be reaching more people than we ever could one-on-one by publishing the books so it all worked out. I am so thankful for this amazing second chance at life I was given!

9

Rewriting Contracts

"Let me keep company always with those who say 'Look!' and laugh in astonishment, and bow their heads."

- Mary Oliver

Now let me share how rewriting contracts went and what it looked like. I think this is a process that can be helpful for anyone going through big physical challenges and changes to help them heal. I hope it might be of use to you on your journey to wellness as much as it was for me.

Identifying Contracts

What are contracts? Contracts are the unspoken and spoken agreements we have with friends and family in our lives. They are sometimes on a spiritual level as well. Contracts define the roles and expectations we have of one another. They control the energy exchange and boundaries we have within a friendship or relationship. A lot of the time we make these contracts without ever speaking of it directly when we choose each other as friends. My role and contract will be different between my immediate family and an acquaintance in my life or between a close friend and a coworker who I like but don't hang out with outside of work. In this way, each person we have in our lives has a different contract with us.

Sometimes, when we get physically sick, things are out of balance. One area that often needs care and attention is energy balance between the people in our lives. When you become sick, you have less extra energy to exchange or waste. You start needing to set more boundaries to protect yourself and to allow yourself time to rest, recharge, and heal. You can't always continue to do the things you used to with people in your life, even the ones who are close to you in your inner circle.

In this download, I saw that I needed to rewrite these contracts starting with those closest to me in the inner circle, and working out to friends, acquaintances, and beyond from there. Later in this chapter is an example of the diagram I made to figure out where to focus first—defining inner circle, middle circle, and outer circle contracts to begin my rewriting of contracts to help get my life back and heal from Lyme disease. Each level has its own boundaries and rules around what I am willing to do and bend or not depending on which level the contract falls in.

See diagram with helpful idea on how to make your own circle of contracts and boundaries.

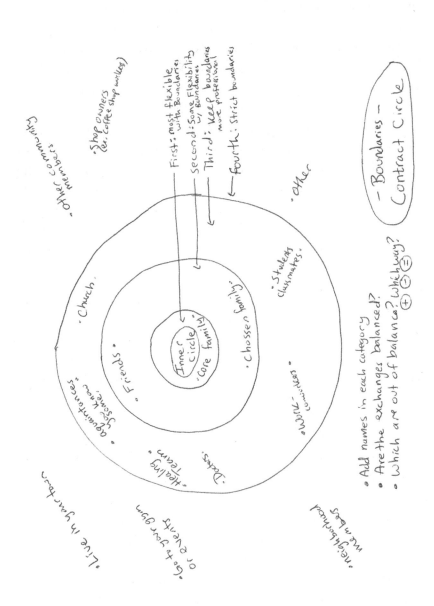

- Boundaries -
Contract Circle

First: most flexible with Boundaries
Second: Some flexibility w/ boundaries
Third: keep boundaries more professional
Fourth: strict boundaries

Inner Circle
· Core family

· Chosen family

"Students / classmates"

· Other

· Work / coworkers

· Friends

· Church

· acquaintances "you know"

· Doctors

· Healing Team

· Shop owners (ex. coffee shop worker)

· Other community

· neighborhood members

· Live in your town

· Got to your gym or event

• Add names in each category
• Are the exchanges balanced?
• Which are out of balance? Whether way? (+) (=) (=)

Assessing How You Recharge: Introvert or Extrovert

The simplest definition of introvert is someone who recharges away from people on their own and who gets their energy by being alone. Extroverts recharge by being with other people. They need connections to feel recharged and energized. Introverts may be good at being with people and enjoy it, but they are just unable to recharge energetically while with people so they need down time and breaks to stay healthy. So you can't judge someone on if they are outgoing or shy. These are not the same as introvert or extrovert. People who are shy are usually carrying a lot of shame and fear about being seen; they might still get recharged by being around people but they are just shy at first. And people who are outgoing doesn't mean they recharge by interacting with people. They have just learned how to be good at communicating with strangers and others because it was safe to do so growing up or culturally.

It is important to recognize these two types of personalities and understand what they need to stay healthy because it is sort of opposite of each other; this is where I found my contracts to be most unbalanced and confused when I met with friends. People assumed I was extroverted because I am outgoing and not shy, but I have always been an extreme introvert when it comes to recharging—I need alone time each day to stay recharged and healthy but as I became an adult, overworking at a career that I loved, it became harder and harder to prioritize alone time to recharge, so my energy level continued to get depleted. I would ramp up on my adrenals to push through and this would hype me up to be more able to be around people when I really needed downtime. Adrenaline pulsed through my veins, allowing my tiredness to disappear. This led to others believing I was extroverted when I never was. The contracts were miscommunicated and confused. I had to rewrite these literally by meeting and having conversations with the people I loved in my life who did not know I was introverted so they wouldn't feel hurt when I would say no to going out or interacting while I was healing and needing more recharge time. I also found that I started meeting my extroverted friends for activities outside like walking or hiking so I was also recharging my physical body through movement while they talked and interacted, getting their energy recharge by being with me. It helped balance the exchange for both of us. So those are some examples of things I changed to get better and create a healthier life through rewriting my contracts.

With someone who you can't talk to—you can rewrite the contract in a journal and/or do it by prayer/talking to the person's higher self and asking spirit, God, source or your guides to help change the contract if they are meant to be in your life still.

As I said previously, I learned I was only up for 1-2 total meet ups with people in a week and I limited each meet up to an hour max over lunch in the middle of the day when I was the least tired adrenal-wise. Crashes usually happened in the afternoon. This is important to repeat because I want you to know to listen to your body and know when you are most recharged and when you are at your weakest energy-wise in a day before planning meet ups with friends or family. Pick the times you know you are usually strongest. Rest in those times of the day you are lower and tired. For me, it was the only task I could do for the day otherwise I would crash in the earlier days of Lyme treatment. Now, years later, I can enjoy seeing more people in a week but it was crucial to give myself that time down and away to recharge and heal in the beginning.

Balancing and Healing Contracts

As I started to work on healing contracts, one of the main goals was recognizing and balancing energy-in to energy-out. Giving and receiving within the relationship needs to be balanced to be healthy and sustainable. Here are some questions I began to ask myself for each person I identified as important enough to have in my diagram.

1. Is this contract balanced:

    - Energetically?

    - Financially?

- Time-wise?

- Listening/talking?

- Physically?

- Emotionally?

2. What do I (we) need to do to make the contract balanced?

3. Is this something that can be fixed? Does it need to be fixed?

4. Is there an introvert v. extrovert need conflict in the contract?

    - Am I an introvert or an extrovert?

5. Is the person I am looking at an introvert or extrovert?

    - How do I feel after I spend time with this person?

    - Am I: Happier? Healthier? Stronger? Energized? Peaceful? Calm? Fulfilled? Joyful?

    - Am I affected either negatively or positively? Am I neutral?

    - Am I shut down? In a shame trance? Worried? Dimmed? Exhausted? Angry? Frustrated?

6. Do I need to speak to this person about the changes that need to happen? Or are they things I can do by changing my boundaries or speaking up for what I need when I need it? Do I need to write them a letter about it?

7. If I need to talk about rewriting the contract to make it work in real life, then set a date and time to meet with the person and have lunch.

What are the first signs that one of my current contracts isn't balanced in some way? My physical health will begin to crash! I get adrenal fatigue symptoms, it becomes harder to ground, I start having symptoms of parasites or I might even see them when I go to the bathroom, not joking! It can be that quick as feedback! It is extremely important for me to stay on my contracts and balance them. I do this through keeping healthy boundaries, asking myself if things feel balanced, and trusting my gut when I don't feel like I should do something with someone or not.

Remember, if you feel anger, it is a sign that a boundary is being crossed in your life. So if you feel anger triggered inside you, stop and ask yourself what boundary is being crossed by that person? Is the contract balanced? Also, know that as you set boundaries and make changes, you will likely experience some extinction bursts with those you love. Extinction bursts are the same concept as when you are treating Lyme; you might feel worse before you feel better. It might get worse (the relationship) before it gets better and becomes healthy. They are die-off pains from the old contract dying and a new one forming. Extinction bursts come in the form of drama or emotions or punishments as a way to try to get you to go back to your old ways and keep the contract unbalanced. So trust they will pass and things will balance out soon enough. Stay true to you and what you need so you can heal and find wellness in your life again. You can't be much of a friend or family member if you're dead.

10

Communicating in the Spirit Realm: Pictures and Collective Consciousness

"Instructions for living a life: pay attention.
Be astonished. Tell about it."

- Mary Oliver

When I say communicating in spirit realm, I am also talking about being in the right mental state and focus to be able to hear and connect to God, spirit or your higher self. This communication comes in a few ways. You might hear words or music. You might see pictures or images or cartoons depicting something or representing something trying to be communicated to you. You might just suddenly know something and find that this knowing is accurate and correct. I like to call these communications with spirit "downloads." Downloads tend to have some specific message that I am supposed to hear and understand or know what to do with. The three downloads I received when I landed back in my body were like this. This type of communication happens in a different time-space reality, so as a human, you may receive a message with much detail in only a second of time on Earth. Trying to speak it or share it after it is received may take minutes to explain with our limited vocabulary and ability to process in the human body. This type of communication can be very fast and detailed and clear if you are in the right state to receive it.

What I learned from this near-death was that this type of communication is all around us, all the time. Each of us has a wealth of information about how we are doing, our physical, emotional, and energetic health, what is important to us, what our life path is, etc. These things are sort of floating throughout the energy field around us; we have just learned to turn off our ability to receive these messages when we are around others so we can better stay present in the physical world as a human on Earth. A lot of this information is not necessary for us in our daily lives so, in essence, our brains learn to filter out the extra "noise" so we can be available to take in what is needed to survive and live. Our bodies are vessels for our spirits to live in and experience our lives on Earth within the limits of time, space, and physical boundaries, giving us experiences that we cannot have as easily in the spirit realm. But we still have access to this type of communication through opening up our third eye. Going into a meditative trance-state frequency in our brain waves can activate it too. During prayer, you can connect to God though this same frequency; it's almost like changing the radio station to a frequency that you can then tune into and understand what is being said. This is the best way to use it for me, to recharge and reconnect with God and spirit and receive downloads and clues as to whether I am on my next right path in my life.

After the near-death, for some reason, my brain wiring was reset enough that I was fully open to receiving these communications and downloads everywhere I went. If I went for a walk around the block, I would get a ton of detailed information about each person I passed, especially their health. I could see it around them in the form of pictures. I would hear words and medical terminology that I had never heard before and would look it up and it was real and existed. I would see colors and shades around their bodies and in their energy field around them. I would just know things from nowhere and found out a lot of the time it was accurate information. This all came to me with no effort at all. It was just there. The hard part was processing the information, which streamed in so fast and so detailed—sometimes it took hours to detangle and process and put into words or communicate from my human body.

With brain fatigue as my main issue from the neurological Lyme and stroke healing, I had very limited amounts of energy to expend each day in the beginning. I would crash, which meant I would have to go into a dark room and go to sleep after small interactions with the world. I had to avoid crowds because I didn't know how to turn the downloads off and, with more than two people near me, the downloads were so loud I would get extremely overwhelmed and completely crash out.

I eventually began to gain back my ability to filter what came in by continuing to expose myself to small groups each day and working to desensitize myself. Like I said earlier in the book, it took almost four years and still wasn't better until I took a class on energy boundaries called Applied Intuition at www.appliedintuition.org. The class taught me how to ground my body and how to build a clear auric field (energy field) boundary which, when I first checked in with mine, I didn't have one anymore.

I had taken this class eight years earlier before I got sick. When I had taken it back then, I had a clear auric field boundary around me. Now it was completely gone and I was inundated and morphing to those around me. No wonder I could take in everyone's energy fields and get so overwhelmed around other people. Once I started to build up

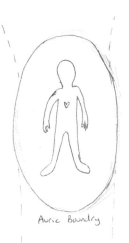

Auric Boundary

my auric field with my intentions and meditations each day, it became easier and easier to be around people again. It was a tool that literally saved my life and allowed me to go to the next stage in my healing from Lyme disease.

I began realizing more and more when talking with others who had Lyme disease that for some reason the infections that came with it tended to cause the auric field to become thinned and weaker. I also realized that if my adrenal glands were more fatigued, my life force energy was down and my field was thinner as well. I was more prone to stressors and energies outside of me. In chapter 12 of this book I share tools for you to try at home to strengthen your auric field and to become aware of downloads so you can better connect to your higher self, spirit, or God and use prayer and meditation as a way to heal faster.

11

Medical Intuition

One of the clear gifts I received from the near-death was the ability to see, hear, and know things about other's health just by being near them or talking to them. I could not turn it off for the first five years after my rebirth. I got better at filtering all the random information coming in as downloads while around people, but the health information still just came through. I would get images and cartoons or hear words or sentences about the person's health I was with. I would just know things, medical terminology and medical diagnoses that I had never been taught or even heard of before, and they ended up being accurate when I looked into them more. I would be driving the car and pass a man walking on the street near me and would suddenly know he was having trouble with his heart, like if he had an atrial fibrillation or high blood pressure. Then I started hearing or seeing things he could do to help fix the imbalance and help him get stronger and not have the disease.

I began to learn that I was picking up on what physical manifestations of health would occur if the energy balance in the field that I was seeing was not rebalanced or addressed. The good news was most of the time you could still do something to make changes to prevent something bigger form happening. The only thing is, a lot of people don't want to take responsibility for their health and honestly don't actually want to get better. Getting better means changing your roles in your contracts with others a lot of the time, and this can just be too much work or too scary for people. We like our emotions, hardships, and drama. They can feel familiar.

I hardly told anyone about this new gift I had. I only told my partner Adam since I was so perplexed and surprised at how accurate it ended up being again and again. For some reason, everywhere I was going I would get people coming to me and sharing with me their fears and health issues, asking for my help without knowing I was seeing these things in their field. I even started having a lot of doctors calling and asking me what I thought about different patients they had. I had not told any of them that I was experiencing these downloads, but somehow in their unconscious brain they knew I knew something and could help. This is because, in reality, our unconscious mind is still getting a lot of this unspoken communication, especially when it is needed. We unconsciously read people, their energy fields, and physical bodies all the time. We assess, judge, predict, and prioritize what is needed or coming up in the future all the time with those around us.

Doctors, therapists, even teachers are expected to be good at reading people. The good doctors tend to have a natural intuition and knowing about what their patients need. This comes from this same area of the brain that perceives the information in our energy field without knowing it—a direct link to spirit and God. It is no longer the limited version of me as a human being but being of service to the higher good, to spirit, to God. Keeping your intention pure and in good alignment with God's grace.

The thing I really learned was that we all have this skill inside us. We all do it all the time and just don't consciously realize it. You might get that gut response to something or just know something inside you. These are the times you have taken in that information from spirit, the downloads. It is not a superpower or anything special; it is just something I got to see and experience with more consciousness because of my brain's need to rewire and heal. It opened my awareness to a skill that we normally are asleep to.

Trust your gut. Trust your inner knowing. It comes from your heart space more than your logical thinking mind. It is just there, and you usually can't explain how you know, but you know it is true in every bone of your body if you don't over think it. That is spirit talking to you; it is God giving you information to help you on your path. You just have to listen and pay attention. For me this means taking time each day to be quiet, still, and away from others where I can pray and do a mediation-type check-in with myself and God and ask for help. This allows me to receive the messages when I need to and not miss them, and also to turn them down or off more easily in my daily life so I am not hearing stuff I do not need to know about others. Only if they ask for help will I open that door.

12

We are All Energy, We are All Light!

"I celebrate myself, and sing myself. And what I assume you shall assume. For every atom belonging to me as good belongs to you."

-Walt Whitman

We are all made of energy. What is energy? It is just the concept of atoms and electrons bouncing around at frequencies creating matter. We are all energy from source just with our own distinct frequencies— our unique energetic fingerprint in a way, our life force. The way I see it is that we all come into this world with a different frequency, which our soul carries. It's like a soul fingerprint in the form of light, which is a frequency itself. I like to think of a prism, and an initial light beam gets sent through that prism and out shoots the rainbow of light in different angles on the other side. We all come from the same initial light (God) before the prism, and we come out of the prism as individual lights with our own unique frequency/colors from that same initial light. All that's changed is our frequency that we're emitting. Because we all have slightly different frequencies, our treatments most likely need to be slightly different depending on what is needed for each individual that is out of balance. You can't treat everyone exactly the same and get the same results.

I am going to call this natural original frequency right out of the prism that we come in with as our unique identity, or our "soul life force energy." When we are in rhythm and sync with this frequency, we feel healthy and full of energy and light and love. When we are out of frequency, we feel off, sometimes sick, out of it, lost, heavy, not ourselves.

Now from here, I move on to the physical body, which is made up of a denser three-dimensional state of mater that carries its own frequency. Our life force energy-spirit merges with the physical body and ideally harmonizes into its own healthy frequency together. The life force energy may need to be lowered to stay grounded inside the physical body, and the physical body will vibrate higher in some areas, which is fine—but some spots can become areas of weakness if they are not integrating well.

When I came back into my body in the MRI machine, I received the ability to see people and the earth as frequency for a while. Everything was vibrating at different frequencies and that is what made the distinction between one thing to the next. When I saw that some-one had a health issue (or was prone to have it in the future), it was because a part of their body would be out of vibration with the area around it and usually at a lower frequency, which caused them to look like they had a cloud of gray or muddy color or heaviness in that area. Now, I am not psychic—everyone can do this if they want to learn and practice, and it doesn't mean the person will definitely get a disease or issue. What I was seeing was the etheric form (the energy body around the human physical body) which shows disease or issues first before coming into the physical body. The "off" area was showing me that there was something not in harmony or sync in this person's frequency in a certain area, and if they didn't change something in how they were living (physically, emotionally, mentally, or spiritually), then they were going in the direction of getting sick or whatever I was seeing.

The good news is being able to see this allowed me to better under-stand how much our thoughts affect our physical bodies, either nega-tively or positively—if negative or traumatic, they bring a heavier denser vibration, if loving and joyful, they carry a higher frequency. Measurable changes in our thymus gland have been documented in multiple studies showing that smiling and joy actually make the thymus gland physically bigger and healthier in our bodies, while negative stress and emotions and infections cause the thymus gland to shrink. Science backs up the fact that what we choose to think and expose ourselves to emotionally affects our physical body more then we could understand. (Diamond, *Your Body Doesn't Lie*)

Frequencies of Thoughts, Beliefs and Prayer

We have the ability with our thoughts and the meanings we attach to things to change the health of our physical bodies from the outside (etheric energy body) in (the physical body) by changing the frequency. Thoughts are real. They carry their own vibration, their own wave lengths, and their own frequency, which means they can change matter. If everything is energy, thoughts are powerful and change things around them, including our bodies. Emotions are powerful too, and our beliefs and prayers matter. Prayer comes from our heart centers into our thoughts and out to God or a higher power. We go to a place of faith and surrender by lowering/dropping stress as we give up our problems or concerns to God to take care of. This faith and surrendering in itself, physically helps us heal by lowering stress in the body. The thymus gland will become bigger and healthier, which in turn increases our immune system drastically.

Frequency of Supplements, Medication and Herbs

Supplements and meds change the frequency of the physical body. If the frequency has taken root in the physical body, then this is one of the ways medicine works to help people heal by shifting the person's frequency by adding the frequencies of the plants in the herbs or medicine. When you ingest and digest them, the frequency is brought into the energy field of your body. It aids you in shifting to a healing state.

I say medications and supplements help people heal, but they don't heal you on their own because it is actually each and every one of *our* own responsibility to heal ourselves. No one else can do it for us.

Others can help facilitate or guide our healing, but they can't heal for us. We have to do the work; we have to believe it will heal us. The power of thought to heal, which is a higher frequency thought of light, comes in and helps heal us or take in the treatments doctors are prescribing. But we choose to take the meds or supplements, which means we are accepting their frequency into our bodies and energy planes. If they don't feel right or aren't working right, then we may decide to stop taking them (or at least talk to our doctors about changing or stopping them, but only stop a medication after talking to a health professional, I am not a doctor). We must ask for help in finding a better match for our healing, for our bodies, and life force energy frequency.

This is one reason why muscle testing, bioenergy testing, and biofeedback can be useful tools in healing from complicated chronic illnesses. One thing that happens in more long-term illness is that we lose our way. We forget how it feels to be in harmony or sync energetically. Then from there it's hard to ground, it's hard to recharge, it's hard to know if something is working. We can feel lost and confused and overwhelmed by our illness, which is our body and energy field vibrating at a different frequency than our natural ideal frequency.

> *One thing that happens in more long-term illness is that we lose our way.*

Like Attracts Like: Mold, Communication and Toxic Environments

While on my healing journey from Lyme, I also found out that I was suffering from mold illness or Chronic Inflammatory Response Syndrome (CIRS). What this meant was that I was being exposed to molds in the buildings where I worked and lived. A lot of the buildings in America have indoor molds, but our bodies are usually functioning well enough to clear themselves of the mold exposures and we don't get sick. But when you have something like Lyme disease and your body's toxic burden becomes overly filled, adding one more thing like mold can be the tipping point and the body is unable to keep up with detoxification quick enough. This leads to a cascade of symptoms and inflammatory related issues in your body. Just like the bugs that I realized each had their own frequency and emotions and things that resonated with them in my life, so did the mold and fungi that was in my living environment.

Adam and I first really became aware of mold as a frequency that could get worse or better in an environment based on emotions and people in the space while living with some housemates. A guest came to stay with us at the house and she was overall very passive aggressive. She was sarcastic and doing things to hurt a roommate of ours and control her. We had a pumpkin on the counter in the kitchen, and during one of the arguments, the pumpkin went from healthy and normal to completely moldy a few hours later. We had noticed ever since this visitor had arrived being passive aggressive to all around her that the house had started to smell of mold, and we were achier and it felt damp. The weather outside was a beautiful dry eighty degrees, so it wasn't from the weather. It seemed to follow this person in the house. This is when we realized passive aggressive energy vibrated at a similar frequency to mold and fungi. They fed each other, resonating with one another.

Passive aggressive thoughts and energy grow mold. Direct communication kills it.

It became even clearer to us that we had to become direct communicators in our own lives to overcome the mold illness. I needed to clean up those contracts to another level by communicating in ways that were direct and not passive. Guess what? It worked! Our housemates jumped on board with us experiencing the same thing we did that week with the visitor, and it helped all of us make our environment in our house healthier and cleaner for healthy, high-frequency living.

The frequency of our communication not only changes the people we are communicating with but the environment in which we live and work in or spend time in. Toxic communication helps toxic biomaterials and substances grow. "Like attracts like" and if we see everything as energy then it is easy to see a thought that is lower vibrationally would help a substance like mold, which is at a lower frequency, flourish and grow.

> *The frequency of our communication not only changes the people we are communicating with but the environment too.*

It's like the saying we hear growing up a lot, "Be careful of who you pick as friends because you become who you are with." And it's true. If you hang around upbeat, optimistic people, you start to shift (literally vibrationally from being around their higher frequency) to a vibration like theirs. If you hang around more negative or passive aggressive friends, then you will begin to shift vibrationally from their waves of frequency by just being near them. So for a short visit, you can hold your own a little better and/or bounce back shaking off their frequency when you leave. If you are around them a lot, then you are more likely to start taking on their vibration and frequency of how they see and experience the world.

I say this with no judgment but simply as an observation to allow you to see that we as human beings and individuals—like we have worked so hard to become in this duality model—have "free will" which is the conscious choice to make the decision of who we want to be.

Stuff is Energy

Physical stuff also holds frequencies. This is one reason they say "ghosts" can be seen as attached to old objects they liked or owned. Or it can be seen as an echo of a vibration left on the stuff. It's just stuck frequency from emotional attachments to the item for whatever reason. Living in an environment with a lot of stuff can carry heavier or confusing frequencies that can shift the health of our physical body. The movement towards simple living, tiny houses, and minimalism is another part of our consciousness shift that is taking place on the earth right now. By removing so much stuff around us, our energy bodies can resonate at higher frequencies without as much resistance. I started to downsize our belongings and spaces with Adam, and it really helped me get stronger. It also helped me kill infections as I deliberately had boundaries with my stuff and chose to let go of past objects and memories by letting go of the items I had been carrying around for years that no longer served me. I t was freeing and healing, and this is another tool you can try using in your healing journey. Work on letting go of stuff in your house and see how it changes how you feel and how your treatments are going. Clearing energy in your home allows for you to heal quicker because you can focus on what is important and rest more fully.

De-clutter your space, de-clutter your energy field!
Help heal your whole body faster!

Making Conscious Choices: Identifying Technological Influences on Healing

In our culture today, we are distracted by TV, news, radio, tablets, the web, cell phones, games, social media, the opportunities, the schools, the jobs, the money . . . And I say this not in a bad way. These are all wonderful and good things if kept in conscious check. The issue isn't the new technology or ways of staying connected, it is in setting boundaries that are healthy for our individual bodies so we stay in balance and hormone-health-wise—chemically, emotionally, spiritually and physically. It can be hard because this stuff is exciting and entertaining and new and tends to be a bit addictive. It stimulates our brains with the reward chemical dopamine and others. It makes us feel good! So the reward neurochemistry keeps us choosing to continue to use stuff when maybe we are actually done or needing to take quiet time or recharge or sleep or eat. It becomes a true distraction from our physical needs, so it's all about being awake to what helps our bodies feel balanced.

"There is no Wi-Fi in the forest,
but I promise you will find a better connection."

-Ralph Smart

Also, just like I shared about how the energy of the people we choose to be around affects our physical and energetic bodies, so does the interactions with all these technology devices, programs, chat rooms, TV shows, movies, etc. Everything is energy. Let me say that again. EVERYTHING IS ENERGY. EVERYTHING has its own set of WAVELENGTHS that it projects.

If the TV show is a story about murder and hate, or people on the show are being passive aggressive, guess what? When you watch it, that frequency is going in and shifting your field. Usually its temporarily when we're healthy, but if you are weakened and sick, you can have more trouble bouncing back to your core healthy frequency. It's that simple. And sometimes it's fun to go into TV for a short time and experience the world of a murderer or experience evil since most of us don't tend to live naturally in that frequency. The key to this is consciously choosing to have that experience and then knowing you aren't going to continue to stay in that frequency by watching that same type of show all the time—because in time you will carry that lower frequency and feel the effects physically in your body if it isn't your natural frequency. This can show up as depression, anger, or you might get issues with toxicity in the body or liver issues, for example. It can land anywhere that you might be weaker or carrying that frequency already as a precursor to physical illness.

This is why when I was healing from the neurological Lyme and the adrenal gland fatigue after the stroke, I would consciously only expose myself to movies or shows that were positive, comedic, joyful, peaceful, or inspirational. I couldn't have surprises or anything that triggered the fight-or-flight response because that energy was already dominating in my body from the illness I was carrying from years of not working on ramping down and healing the traumas I had experienced as a kid. We all hold trauma somewhere in our bodies from life and these are the weak spots that can become bigger when we watch things that mirror that frequency. Sometimes we purposefully or unconsciously choose to expose ourselves to those similar frequencies because our body and unconscious mind wants us to find and work on healing these old stored traumas (frequencies hiding in our bodies). These frequencies no longer serve us but they are so stuffed and unreachable it is the only way to light them up in us in a way by making them bigger so we can see them and find them and work on healing them. If you can't find or see the issue, then there is no issue to work on. But it can feel like an elephant sitting in the room of our body/spirit and mental health, and we can't seem to find it without the help of exposing ourselves to those frequencies that mirror it. "Oh, that's it! I found my issue!" Meanwhile, my physical body may now have some real health issues on the physical level. Once I work through this emotional block and I can get the right treatment on board, then hopefully I can heal.

Strike a Pose: Change Your Posture. Change Your Mood!

A great tool to use that is super simple and really works is the idea of shifting our posture to shift our mood and energy. Sometimes just shifting our physical bodies, literally changing our posture, can change our frequency. For instance, looking up instead of down has been found in multiple studies to increase happiness and optimism, while looking down caused depression and hopelessness. Another way to change our energy and how we feel is by changing our location, which can also shift our frequency. Or we can change the people we are choosing to spend time with to shift our frequency. Because energy/frequency is made of waves, being near other's waves interacts with our waves and vice versa, so we are actually changing our wave when the two collide and overlap. It's not better or worse—its matching to the frequencies that help you stay in and be in that optimal life force frequency that allows for good health in the physical body while you are on Earth.

Some people resonate with lower frequencies and are here to work in that frequency, while others need much higher frequencies to stay healthy. When I use the words lower and higher, these come from our world of duality which we still live in, and I want you to know higher doesn't mean better and lower doesn't mean worse—it is just the type of waves which we choose to live in and what feels right for our soul frequency. There is no judgment, just an acknowledgement that everyone has their role in the game of life, and I appreciate what they are here to do and can trust they know what is best for their soul's path.

Power of Choice and Waking Up

Once we realize the power in choice and free will when we are sick, we can choose to put ourselves with those who have an energy frequency that resonates with good health in us and in environments that are in alignment with our healthy life force frequency. When we do this, we start to heal from our health ailments physically much faster. I call it super speed. And it works!

That's it. Consciously choosing what type of energy frequency to put ourselves around can actually heal our physical bodies as much as taking an antibiotic or medication to treat our physical ailments. This is why I am bringing this up in this book, to help others wake up to the power of choice in their daily lives as to who they put themselves around or where they spend their time and how it affects the healing of their physical bodies.

> *Choosing what type of energy frequency we put ourselves around can actually heal our physical bodies almost as much as taking supplements and medications, and it's something you can do at any time.*

Waking up to the power of our thoughts and choices is huge. Sometimes it is scary for people to realize that they are responsible for their own healing, or that they are choosing to stay sick or get better in terms of their daily life activities and what they do to help themselves get better. The rest is spiritually letting it go and praying with faith for help. I am not saying anyone decides "I want to feel horrible and stay sick" or that it is your fault at all. No, what I am saying is once you wake up to these concepts, you realize you can heal and that all it takes are some baby-step changes to start the ball rolling. These steps have to do with experimenting and getting to know yourself and what makes you feel stronger and what makes you feel weaker in your body. What raises your life force energy and your spirit's strength, and what weakens it and drains you. This is essentially what muscle testing and biofeedback scanning are testing and showing you.

Energy Frequency of Infections

During my treatment and healing I found that each infection carried its own frequency that connected to different emotions. For example, when treating and killing Bartonella it would cause me to have intense fear and loss of hope in my body and mind. I would actually hear in my mind "you should just give up; you're going to die anyway." This would get louder as I continued treatment at first until it suddenly would stop. This is when the die off stopped, and I had killed the infection enough that it wasn't trying to stop me from taking my meds and doing my treatments. This is something I experienced and researched through blogs and online forums finding the same exact wording was being heard by many other people going through Bartonella treatment. I found that Bartonella resonated with fear in my body, wherever I had traumatic stored emotions of fear in my body specifically for me my nerves. As I treated the Bartonella I also worked on identifying and healing the fear trauma stored in my body and mind. Suddenly the treatment time was accelerated tenfold and it worked. I had been blocked and plateaued but now I was able to heal and move on to another infection. The medications started to work better once I had identified the emotional frequency that first attracted the Bartonella to those spots in my body. Like attracts like- by removing the energy that was similar frequency to Bartonella- fear, I was able to then treat it physically with medication and keep it away.

Each infection has its own frequency so to kill them you need to know what will be most efficient and help the body do its job in getting to each of them in the right order. Some frequencies block others, so the order in which you treat chronic infections when the body is overwhelmed is key in making the journey gentler, smoother, and efficient.

For example, parasites can block your body's ability to treat Lyme disease and most people with Lyme have co-infections, which include multiple parasitic infections. So if you treat the parasites first and then focus in on the Lyme, you're not wasting the meds (which are frequencies) that kill Lyme. The body can't even use these if it needs to treat parasites, which are a different frequency, first.

It's like the concept of peeling back the layers on an onion. You can't just peel the core first; you have to work from the outside in, otherwise it's a mess and overwhelming for the onion and your eyes trying to cut into it from the center out!

Muscle testing, which I talk about in the next section, allowed my body to communicate about which infection and systems in my body were most stressed and needed treatment and attention first with my doctor. He got the report and was able to then put me on detoxification support so that when we went in to eradicate and kill the pathogens, my body could handle the toxic burden that the bugs produce as they die. As we discussed in a previous chapter, this die-off is like a small extinction burst and releases neurotoxins, biotoxins, endotoxins, and other toxins that your body's immune system reacts to as a foreign invader, which temporarily increases inflammation and makes you feel sicker before you feel better. It is a way the pathogens try to stop you from taking the medication or supplement that is working to kill them, hoping you will stop the treatment thinking it's not working because you feel worse when on it.

If you can become awake to this concept, then you can better understand that the Herxheimer effect (aka die-off) will only be temporary. Once the pathogens die down (no pun intended), then you will actually feel stronger and better without that bug inside you anymore, shifting your natural vibrant life force frequency. It is very important to not push too hard or too fast with your treatments. If you are having die-off symptoms, this means you may need more detox support and time to clear out before killing more, or use a lower dose and work up to a higher one. You will hopefully be working with a skilled doctor who knows the complications of Lyme treatment and can help you monitor and go slow in the beginning, working up so you don't have much die-off at all. I had a few visits to the ER doing too many treatments at once and getting really sick from the die-off before knowing and understanding this slow and steady concept.

As I mentioned at the beginning of this section, these bugs carry their own frequencies that shift us out of resonance with our health frequency. This is what the bioenergetic testing picks up on, as well as the muscle testing. And it is what I was able to see and perceive after I died and came back. We all are able to see this—we just are trained not to as we grow up. I could see we were all waves of energy and frequency and everything effects everything else, just to various levels, and it can be for better or for worse. Culturally, we are told it is wrong and what to perceive, and it disappears so we can fit in.

You've Got Tools: Muscle Testing/Bioenergetic Testing

Finding a naturopathic doctor or integrative doctor who uses muscle testing, or bioenergetic testing, as part of your treatment is a great resource to learn more about your body and what makes you stronger or weaker. If you feel stronger, it means you are more in resonance with that treatment or thought or whatever you were testing. You can test environments by bringing in a glass jar of the air from them. I also found it helpful when they muscle tested and found I was stressed in an area of my body; they could then order labs or scans that ended up being more relevant and showed results instead of randomly guessing or ordering too many things. They also muscle tested all my medications and treatments as I went along on my healing journey. They would change my dose or the type of supplement or medication I was taking depending on what MY body needed, not just guessing. They used their research-based educations as doctors but also mixed in their knowledge and wisdom with what my body presently showed it needed (or didn't need), taking their egos out of the process. I took more responsibility for taking my meds and supplements because I could feel how they made my body stronger during the testing. It motivated me to make the changes, knowing they were working.

If it is hard for you in the beginning to know what you feel or who you are then going to see a practitioner that uses muscle testing or energy feedback can be helpful in learning more about how to read your own body. They can teach you about what things are making you weaker or stronger just by being in the energy fields of those objects, and this includes supplements, meds, and thoughts. It can wake you up to being able to read your own body's needs for balance. It's amazing to feel the power of the object's frequency near you, or the thought we hold when we can't hold our own arm up even if we try our hardest. When we have thoughts that help our body or supplements that test well, our body (which felt weak and fatigued a minute earlier) is now strong and able to withstand a lot of force. The smallest shifts can really change our physical body's ability to be healthy, be literally strong, and also go into a strong healing state.

This is a great way to play with this concept of how much the energy body affects the physical body. You also get to know how to read your own needs so that you can become more awake and choose to put things that make you stronger around you and put up clear boundaries around things that make you weaker. This is the gift of free will and choice and having a voice in our lives, which helps us heal even faster!

Once I realized this concept of healing, my completely torn-up, rattled physical body suddenly started to heal faster than any of my doctors could have ever expected. Once I understood that whoever I chose to be around affected my energy body frequency and the environment I lived in, I had the ability to make some clear choices that would aid my physical body in the fight for its life just by putting up some boundaries and changing how I was living. Now, remember, I had just died and come back. I'd had a stroke. My adrenal glands were no longer functioning well. My immune system was so out of whack from being out of resonance with my energy body that I was carrying a lot of parasites, multiple species of Lyme and coinfections inside it. I was whacked out to say the least! So if I can accelerate my healing just by focusing in on energy and what made me stronger or weaker and trying to cut out the weaker forces and incorporate in more of the stronger ones, then anyone can do it!

Build Up Your Energy Body Awareness and Tools to Reset Your Energy Field

Take an Intuition Class

Taking an intuition or clairvoyance class is a great way to start. These classes are taught at a variety of places around the country, and world. They usually have a beginner's class at most places that offer similar skill sets like the following:

1. How to ground yourself every day with a grounding cord, grounding tools and visualizations. How to bring in grounding energy from the earth and cosmic energy from spirit.

2. How to clear your auric field and create a clear auric boundary that tucks into your grounding cord. You may learn how to put up some protections when you feel more vulnerable or tired around your auric field.

3. They may teach you about the seven basic chakras and how to clear them.

4. They may teach you about how to run different types of colors and light frequencies in your auric field to help heal things or change energy frequencies in your field.

Class Resource

Tahara Ezrahti of Applied Intuition offers classes in person and online through zoom (https://www.appliedintuition.org). What I like about her classes and how she teaches is she really focuses on how anyone can learn these skills and she doesn't make it a religion or belief. She teaches you tools to hone in on abilities and skills we already inherently have when we are born and just haven't been taught to use. So, no matter what you believe religion-wise, you can do these things just by being a human. It's just like reading a book or how to write or run or jump. It's that simple. It just uses a different area of our brain than we are normally trained to use since childhood.

Strengthening your brain's waves for energy awareness and healing the brain

Meditation became one of the biggest ways I was exercising my brain; to stay in a state of quiet focus while letting go and bringing my attention to the center of my head and heart or focus on my breath. I also found listening to fifteen-minute visualization meditations was a ton of exercise for my brain to focus that long and relax into them. I have some meditations for download on my website if you are wanting to try any of them: www.carolinedeloreto.com

Hu

Using the "Hu chant" for shifting into higher frequency if stuck lower. Hu is a chant that resonates at the frequency of God. It is similar to the heart frequency. This can shift lower frequencies into ones of love just by singing and chanting it, helping your body shift to that frequency too or the room you are in.

Singing bowl sound therapy

You can use singing bowls with different frequencies to clear your energy field or reset after being in crowds.

Strengthen your grounding

You can use water to help you ground or literally reset your energy. Take showers, baths, or get near or into an ocean, lake, swimming pool, or other body of water. Taking a walk barefoot on the grass, earth, or sand can ground you, especially near a body of water or standing next to big trees. Lying on the ground on a blanket can ground your body quickly too.

Posture

Change your posture, change your life! The position you put your body and head in can shift your physical state, emotional state, and overall frequency. What a great and controllable tool you can play with to change your frequency and mood! It doesn't require talking through things or with others, it just takes moving your physical body into new positions. The better the posture, the better your health can be! And it's not just posture, but also facial expressions and eye movements.

If you are more slumped over or out of alignment, then it has been shown in studies that you will have more depression, your thymus gland will be less active and shrinks, you will feel less optimistic, and you will have less of your personal life force energy flowing into your body. If you straighten your spine and look straight ahead—or even better slightly up with your eyes—it activates the brain to release chemicals that aid in happiness, optimism, and feelings of joy. It also increases the health and size of your thymus gland, which is extremely important to your immune system and increases your life force, also known as chi, in your body. Play with this in your daily life—try out different postures and see how you feel in them.

13

Theory of Lyme as Catalyst for Spiritual Development

*"It is during our darkest moments
that we must focus to see the light."*

-Aristotle

Congratulations, you are on your way to spiritual awakening and ascension just by being on the path you are on living with the challenges of chronic illness or Lyme disease right now. You probably want to knock me upside the head for seeing it as a celebration, but if you can learn to embrace the fact that to heal from something as big as Lyme disease (or COVID-19 or an autoimmune disease or cancer or any other chronic illness), you will be forced to look deep within and heal on many levels—physical, emotional, spiritual, and energetic.

This means you have to heal places in your body where you have lower frequency vibration states so that you can return and find a higher frequency of wellness overall in your body and energy field. In other words, you are fully going into a state of accession and spiritual growth to get there.

It is also like your own mini "hero's journey" which as you know always has its challenges, pain, and something to overcome before the hero becomes a hero. You are doing this just on a soul level, climbing up the ladder of frequency and energy to one of light and love.

To do this you must shed those frequencies that are lower like emotional and physical traumas stored in your body and field, shame, patterns that you have outgrown, rewriting contracts with those in your life to be healthier and more balanced, prioritizing how you spend your time and energy on Earth, and finding your soul's purpose at the core. It takes prayer, faith, surrender, and trust in the greater good and plans for our lives from a soul understanding and God. This all happens as you are treating your physical body and healing with medicine and support systems. How exciting!

I believe that Lyme is a catalyst for spiritual ascension as individuals and as part of the greater shift of our Earth right now from lower frequency to a higher one. Lyme disease is everywhere and affecting so many people, and many don't even know they have it yet. But we are starting to see how much it's affecting our world with celebrities and athletes coming out of the woods to share their journey to the masses. COVID-19 is another example of an illness that is acting as a catalyst for our spiritual accessions as a culture, world, and individuals. And with the continued decline in oxygen in our environment, we will only be seeing more illness and diseases creeping up in the near future. Oxygen is crucial to our health, and with the oceans being so polluted and overfished, the ecosystems in the ocean that create most of our oxygen are being destroyed much more rapidly than they can rebuild. I am not trying to project doom about this, it's just a reality that is going to be forcing us to wake up more spiritually through the hardships of illness. All experiences are just that: experiences. They are here to teach us and help us grow. Then universe, God, or source, is using these challenges as a way to wake us up spiritually and find connection to spirit.

My own personal experience with Lyme disease and healing from it catalyzed me into a complete spiritual overhaul and awakening, and I have seen the same sort of awakening in almost every person I have worked with who has Lyme disease.

I have seen atheists turn spiritual when they see there is a higher power at work again and again. I have witnessed people giving up the career path they were on to instead be of service in another more meaningful way as part of their healing, and suddenly that shift is what triggers their final healing from Lyme physically. They are choosing to be of service in hope to bring more light to Earth.

Most people with Lyme disease have multiple areas of their life that need changing and clearing. It sort of acts as a spiritual cleanser and decluttering device. Because Lyme makes you more tired energy-wise, you have to decide and prioritize what you put your energy into each day of your life. You start cutting out the things that are draining or not important. You sort through which relationships are balanced or not energetically, and you are forced to identify toxins and toxic relationships in your life, including work, doctors, friends, and family. You start rewriting contracts with all those in your life naturally, and this changes you spiritually and begins to bring you to a higher frequency vibration. This is how Lyme acts as a catalyst in our individual ascension process and the greater shift of the world right now.

Interconnected

The ascension process is a spiritual growth process in which you realize that we are all interconnected and there is a collective consciousness involved in all we do as well. Some call it source or God. We all affect each other and can help each other just by working on our own health and personal growth. Literally, if all you can do is take care of yourself physically and emotionally and spiritually, then you will be helping the collective consciousness go up in frequency and ascension, and that is the purpose that is needed right now since we are moving toward a heart frequency, much closer to what Jesus Christ resonates at, what God resonates at.

So if you are struggling with health challenges that leave you disabled in ways you weren't earlier in your life, or you feel like you are beating yourself up inside for not having any worth or purpose on Earth any longer, or you just feel like a burden, please remember this: You are important, you are loved, and you have purpose just by waking up each day and doing your best to get your own life force energy frequency up. You becoming healthy in a state of wellness is helping us all, since all our energies affect each other! Thank you! And it's hard to remember or hear this when we have a society full of technology and advertisements and media bombarding us with "shoulds" and "coulds" and what we "need to be" to be great.

The truth is you are perfect just the way you are. And in accepting who you are and giving yourself love, you are sending love and light out to the world and helping it shift to a higher state of being. By accepting all of yourself, you are giving others permission to be themselves, and you will be able to better see them and love them since you will have more love to give. You are part of the shift! Every one of us is, and each of us counts! We need you.

Plus, it can be really fun once you start connecting more and more into the ascension process. Your spiritual awakening and growth can blow your mind and bring new perspectives to the world and the way you saw it before you got sick. It's a gift that I am not willing to give up to go back to a time before I had Lyme. My life is so much more full from this process, even though it was extremely difficult, confusing, painful, and scary at times. Looking back, it was worth it.

Faith in Each of Our Souls Knowing

Another thing Lyme taught me is having faith in my soul's knowing and in the bigger picture at a soul level. The more I do this work, the more I realize that all of our souls know what they are doing and I have learned to trust that each person's soul knows what it's doing. The way to ascension and healing sometimes needs the individual to go through some sort of challenge or big healing crisis or accident to act as the catalyst to propel them ahead in their spiritual growth. It's so big or life-changing that it forces and allows the person to let go of all those smaller things that weigh us down and block us from knowing what is truly important to us at a soul level. The challenge from our health gets rid of the many "distractions" in today's world, like putting our faith in our possessions or technology instead of a higher power/ God, and being "too busy" all the time and trying to be "successful" living the American dream.

I find that the caretaker and rescuer inside me that wants to help others by fixing them is easy to turn off now if I can remind myself and tell myself, "I trust that each person's soul knows what it is doing in their life journey." I want to give them the message that I believe in *their* ability to heal or deal with their challenges, and that God has plans for them. It is not my place to rescue them from it, especially if they haven't asked for help. I then can trust that they will be ok, pray for them, and more importantly, tell their soul that I believe *they can do it.*

Sometimes we forget that by trying to fix someone or help them when they can do it for themselves, we can actually be harmful—we unconsciously tell their soul that we don't believe they can do it, that they are not well enough or equipped enough. In truth, we all have the ability to heal and do our work. It is better to help only when asked directly. I do send out prayers and light and love to people when I am having the urge to do something for them instead of doing it without being asked.

In other words, illnesses, health challenges, diagnoses and traumas can all be ways "spirit/God" kicks our butts into gear in the ascension process. No matter how hard it gets, if you can remember that they are all just moments and they will pass and there will be a day where you see and feel lighter again, then you will find healing will catalyze faster. Hold on and hang in there. What doesn't kill you makes you stronger, and it makes you who you are with more understanding, compassion, and experience to then be present and understanding of others.

Wake Up Call – Identity Rebirth

Sometimes to make bigger changes in our lives, like retiring or changing careers, we have to change what we see as who we are. We go through an emotional identity rebirth with or without physical health acting up. More times than not, our physical health does get worse with these changes and acts as a catalyst for us to make the change happen with more power behind it. For me, I had to lose my memory completely and then have a stroke to really wake me up! Wake me up to make the changes and get out of the nervous system patterns and lifestyle patterns I had built for the 32 years I had already been alive. I had been a type-A extremely busy bee, caretaking and doing all the time. I loved it. Now I couldn't. I was forced to slow down and change due to the memory and physical health issues.

I had to stop my work as a middle school teacher and learning specialist for fifteen years, disconnect from the community of people I worked with daily and saw as my chosen family, which I wouldn't have been able to leave if I hadn't been forced by my health. Looking back on it, the truth was that for a few years leading up to my health crash, on a spiritual level I had outgrown the work I was doing there. It was no longer what my soul needed to be doing to learn and I needed to make the change way before the physical symptoms began. I was comfortable, though. I enjoyed my work and found it rewarding. I knew how to do my job and I loved the people and students I worked with. I had no motivation to make the jump even though I had received many messages inside that it was time to move on for my own growth. I ignored them and continued doing what I was used to because it was easier that way. It was known, and the unknown was too scary.

I was also forced to slow down and learn how to ramp down and live in a parasympathetic lifestyle. I wasn't willing to slow down. I didn't know anything other than being "ramped up" and running on my adrenals. I loved how I felt because I could get so much done in a day all the time. I had so much energy and was going all the time. I woke up early and worked all day and I exercised daily, read books, took classes, traveled and raised our niece on top of 14-hour workdays. I was ramped up and didn't know it. With my sympathetic nervous system dominant, running on adrenaline, dopamine, and endorphins, my body thought I was in some sort of crisis or danger when it was really just my choice to keep so busy.

It was just who I was, constantly moving and needing stimulation, and I didn't know how to be any different. Stillness was not something I knew how to do. And I had no reason to seek it. I recharged by being by myself, but even when on my own, my mind would keep me very busy and entertained by making lists, goals, dreams, and trying to read, write, and do everything I could in my time on Earth. Not a stone stayed unturned. I was the energizer bunny until I wasn't. LOL.

We Are All Light and Love at the Core

We are all pure white energy of love and light when we are born. Then, over time, we gather experiences, good and bad. Some shade us and dim our original light. Things like shame or fear, for example, dim our light in our field. This is important to understand because when we have areas in our field that are dimmer, this is a lower frequency and is more prone in our physical body to show up as illness later since like attracts like and illnesses and infections tend to have lower frequency vibrations.

If we see pure love and light as white light, the highest frequency of all, then the shame you carry would be a lower frequency in you that has less light coming from it, so it's not a matter of a darker energy coming in—it is a dulled down light or a fog that hovers around you.

We are all light at the core—beautiful pure bright white light when we start out. God's light. Then things like our physical bodies and the alignments they come with dim some of that, then the things our family and friends give us or don't give us shifts that light some more, and how we mentally and emotionally experience life shifts it. When we come into our physical bodies, we are this pure light, but the bodies we come into already have their own energies and densities and so this shades us and colors us right off with the physical matter we come into. But overall, you will start off with your most pure light as a child before society and programming take place on Earth.

So the core of what I am trying to explain is that when we have an emotion like shame, which is something causing us to hide our true light, it literally dims and hides our light. The frequency of the light at the core is lowered and dimmer. This invites like-frequency things to it, such as parasites or infections or mold (mold grows and lives best in dimmer, less-light-filled spaces, right?), so they end up matching us frequency-wise in the areas we have shame. The natural law of like attracts like applies here—without realizing it, we end up inviting mold into our bodies, or into our living spaces, and it feels familiar and the same so at first we won't even notice, and it might even feel comfortable and homey to be in it. It resonates with us. Because it literally does.

Now as you start to clean up your shame in your life through therapy or self-growth work, this is when a "healing crisis" can take place. Suddenly you are starting to shift that dimmed frequency of light in your energy field and body as you become awake to the shame inside you, and this shifts your frequency with your outside environment you live in and interact with.

Suddenly there are "die off" reactions on both sides—the home that felt so safe and balanced to you now is making you sick. You are having mold illness symptoms and you are fighting to figure out why suddenly you feel sick. People around you who you unconsciously chose because "like chooses like" (and who know the rules of your movie) get upset that you are changing and have "extinction bursts," as we call them in family therapy land. They start feeling hurt, or they try to shame you more to control you back into your old frequency. Stop changing! Not allowed! Because then I have to change and I was comfortable as it was . . . You see, as you shift into light frequency, the things around you do too (or need to) if you are going to stay together in life.

An example can be seen when I was working on treating parasites in my body and I started to clean up my boundaries with some of my friends. I realized a few friendships were really one-sided with me giving and them taking energy, so I had to decide if I was going to keep these people in my life or not, and if I did want to, then I had to decide how I wanted to change these dynamics to make them more balanced and have boundaries with my time and energy while with them.

As I did this work, parasites actually started dying—I would see them come out of me literally when I went to the bathroom the day after starting to clean up these contracts without taking any new meds. This has happened countless times for me now. If I start to have symptoms of parasites or seeing them, then I always stop and ask myself where in my life am I in parasitic relationships and what needs rebalancing? This shifts the energy in my gut from one of parasitic imbalance (lower frequency) to one of harmony and love (for myself) and brings my frequency up to a state of wellness and healing vibration.

The Lyme or physical illness is acting as a catalyst for you to do your spiritual purging and clearing and ascending to a space of higher frequency and light. Spiritual and conscious awakening and growth. You realize the power you do have is to become more present and conscious in your everyday choices and life. And make space for what is important and lower the distractions from your everyday busy grind where you most likely were unconscious most the time.

Slowing down, simplifying your life, and choosing quality over quantity of activities leads to happiness and success. You start purging energetic vampires and drains, and you also begin to clear out and let go of stuff in your life that is junking it up. Minimalism and decluttering can be very helpful in this process, and I have found that a lot of people going through these health challenges have found decluttering their physical life can help them declutter their energetic bodies and minds and let go of emotional and traumatic baggage they were holding onto inside of them. This also allows for more ascension to occur, more light to come in, and light to be shared outwardly.

So this is one reason I think these challenging experiences are acting as healing catalysts and its why they have come in—they propel a person through these stages faster and almost force them to let go, detach, and realize they are not in control. It allows you to let go of ego and identity quicker so you can live form a heart place instead of a mental place.

An accident, a terminal diagnosis, a chronic un-diagnosable infection or illness, a sudden environmental crisis like a fire, earthquake, or tornado comes through your life—literally all these things uproot you and shift your energy so fast you can't fight it. It may feel like a "dark night of the soul" type of path you are on and like there is never going to be light at the end of the tunnel—and you are right, it won't be at the end of the tunnel. Instead, it will be right inside you starting at your heart and it will shoot out of the top of your head and you will feel brighter than you ever have since you were a baby. You will have been reborn, and as an adult, you get to start again with fewer triggers, a reset nervous system, and a new level of compassion, empathy, love, openness, and curiosity for the world than you ever had, or at least since you were a young child.

When we can see our greatest challenges, like Lyme, as a gift or a catalyst, then we take back our power and create light out of darkness, setting us free from the lower frequency of illness and moving us each up into a healing state of wellness!

"Someone I loved once gave me a box full of darkness. It took me years to understand that this too, was a gift."

- Mary Oliver

PART II

The Diamond of Healing Philosophy

The Journey

–Mary Oliver (Devotions p.316, Penguin Press, NY 2017)

One day you finally knew
what you had to do, and began,
though the voices around you
kept shouting
their bad advice–
though the whole house
began to tremble
and you felt the old tug
at your ankles.
"Mend my life!"
each voice cried.
But you didn't stop.
You knew what you had to do,
though the wind pried
with its stiff fingers
at the very foundations,
though their melancholy
was terrible.
It was already late
enough, and a wild night,
and the road full of fallen
branches and stones.
But little by little,
as you left their voices behind,
the stars began to burn
through the sheets of clouds,
and there was a new voice
which you slowly
recognized as your own,
that kept you company
as you strode deeper and deeper
into the world,
determined to do
the only thing you could do–
determined to save
the only life you could save.

14

Introduction Part II

The Diamond of Healing is a layout for my philosophy on healing. I have developed this philosophy as a way for the reader to better understand all the different aspects to healing from Lyme and chronic illness based on my own experiences. If you follow the different sides and consider the things I bring up for each, you will find that you will begin to feel better in time.

Sometimes it feels easier to focus on one side more then another. You can use this to help you find what areas you maybe weaker in or needing to pay attention to and get ideas of options to make shifts in your lifestyle to heal faster. Sometimes just being able to identify what is not working and what is working can help us shift into a state of healing. Getting unstuck and being able to take back our power by knowing what to focus on can be helpful on its own. The first step in healing is becoming conscious and aware that there is a problem or that we are sick. The next step is knowing what to do about it and doing it. And the third step is asking for help. Asking for help when we are stuck and lost, too overwhelmed or can't do it for ourselves any longer.

I hope the Diamond can help you find the areas you need to balance and focus on and connect to a healing team of health practitioners to receive the treatments you need for Lyme or any other chronic illnesses you may be struggling with. Most of this can be applied to any illness or disease, not just Lyme. My goal is to help you have a tool to assess where you are unbalanced so you can be empowered to take back your health and life to a state of wellness again!

DIAMOND OF HEALING:
4 SIDES OF THE DIAMOND OVERVIEW

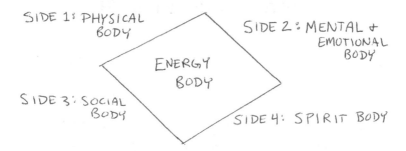

Goal: To reach a healing frequency in your energy body throughout each day. Living in a state of wellness having inner peace and joy in your heart.

How do you do this?

You do this by adjusting the 4 sides of the diamond that make up your "whole" body health through:

1. Balancing Your Physical Body

    - Taking supplements or medications when needed to help your physical body catch up and rest when it is depleted or too stressed.

    - Making lifestyle changes to include exercise, good sleep hygiene, balanced nutrition, and detoxification support.

    - Building and seeking support of a "healing team."

    - Educating yourself about your body so you can make choices to help yourself heal faster and ask for help.

2. Balancing Your Mental and Emotional Body

   - Changing your mindset about your life and healing.

   - Identifying and changing the meaning of events that have caused you stress in your life.

   - Implementing lifestyle changes. Lowering chronic stress.

   - Visualizing and meditating on what you want your life to be when you are better: What does it look like? Feel like? How are you different? How are you the same? Really paint the picture of healthy you and all you want to do with your life.

   - Rewriting contracts with all those in your life- rebalancing the energy exchange. Plug the holes and drains!

   - Balancing your emotions and environments in which you spend your time.

   - Taking responsibility for your life, healing, and future.

   - Empowering you to lead your life and walk in alignment with your true self.

   - Finding a stronger sense of self and building your life force back.

3. Balancing Your Social Body

   - Building a supportive community through your work, friends, and family.

   - Practicing honest and open communication with your partner or family while in treatment.

   - Asking for help when you need it.

   - Getting out to do things that bring you joy, not isolating completely while feeling sick.

   - Identifying and acting on taking your place in the world!

- Choosing healthy relations with people in your life and setting boundaries when needed to support your wellness.

4. Balancing Your Spirit Body

   - Finding a community or support system for your spiritual needs- Church, spiritual groups, friends, meet ups.

   - Reading books that inspire your connection to your higher power, spirit, and God.

   - Identifying your purpose and life path and following it.

   - Finding your purpose and living in alignment with who you are at your core without anyone outside of you "shoulds."

   - Learning tools to help you ground and connect to spirit and your higher self.

   - Choosing to live in alignment with your purpose and path.

5. Center of the Diamond

   - The Energy Body, which is affected by all sides of the diamond. If you balance the 4 sides, the energy body will become clearer and stronger. Your life force will increase, and you will feel more vibrant and well.

PART II
SIDE 1 OF THE DIAMOND

Physical Body

15

Side 1: Physical Body

The Serenity Prayer

"God grant me the serenity
To accept the things I cannot change;
Courage to change the things I can;
And wisdom to know the difference.
Living one day at a time;
Enjoying one moment at a time;
Accepting hardships as the pathway to peace."

-Reinhold Niebuhr

In this section I will be going into the different things you can focus on to help support your Lyme treatment and healing. The first and very important step is to build your Healing Team- the health practitioners who will guide you on your treatments for Lyme and all it comes with.

(Please Note: I am using the term "Lyme" to describe both Lyme and co-infections and all that comes with it. When you have Lyme it rarely comes by itself- it is married to other co-infections and issues. To make writing simpler throughout this book I use Lyme in this way a lot.)

Building Your Healing Team: Trust, Safety, Support

One thing anyone who has had Lyme knows is that you can feel very alone and isolated by the medical field, your families and friends who don't understand, and by our culture's preconceived beliefs about

Lyme. It is so important to take the time to build a Healing Team you can trust and feel safe with knowing they have your best interest in all of their suggestions. Each person has different focus areas so it is up to you to decide who you want to invite to join your team, and who you may not need. It is a revolving door in a sense, you can add or drop anyone depending on what you need to get to the next level of healing. It's important to feel like they are supportive and adding to your healing state not making you feel worse about having Lyme.

Here is a list of Suggested Team Members to Find:

1. Lyme disease Specialist Doctor - "Integrative" would be preferred.

2. Primary Care Doctor who believes in Lyme and will be supportive of your treatment.

3. Naturopathic Doctor who knows about or is open to treating Lyme. They may offer IV's, oxygen therapies, alternative therapies and nutritional support as well.

4. Therapist/Counselor or group support. Interview them to see if they know about Lyme and believe in it before signing on for support.

5. Massage therapist - someone who offers Swedish massage and gentle lymphatic drainage options. Doing deep massage work can push detoxification too fast when in treatment for Lyme and make you feel sicker.

6. Homeopathic Practitioner who knows about Lyme and will support you with your healing team.

Other specialists you may want to add and find:

Neurologist, Acupuncturist, Acupressurist, Physical Therapist, Endocrinologist, Cardiologist, Nutritionist, Chiropractor, Osteopathic doctor, etc...

1. **Lyme Specialist Doctor - Integrative Preferred.** Overall most good Lyme specialists are integrative doctors. This means they usually are allopathic doctors who have also trained in natural or eastern medicine and they integrate modalities of treatment into their practice. Or they are naturopathic doctors that are trained in western and eastern modalities as well. The main concept is they integrate multiple ways to treat each patient so they can more fully help your unique body heal from Lyme. Using herbs, prescriptions, physical body manipulations and mind-body connection exercises are things that integrative doctors are more likely to know about and use to treat the whole person. The key is being sure that they know about and specialize in Lyme. They usually are members of the International Lyme and Associated Diseases Society (ILADS) or have gone through some sort of training for the complications people with Lyme disease may face. Make sure they know about co-infections, environmental toxin issues, and detoxification in the body.

2. **Primary Care Doctor.** A primary care doctor is there to oversee all areas of your health and get specialists when you need them. The key here is to find a primary care doctor who knows about Lyme disease, or at least isn't closed minded about it. You want someone you feel safe calling up to ask for referrals when you need them since Lyme can be a great imitator and move from one area in the body to another. You usually end up seeing multiple specialists in different areas. Sometimes you have a primary care doctor and still end up spending most of your time working with your chosen Lyme specialist or Naturopathic doctor. That is fine!

3. **Naturopathic Doctor (ND).** Having a ND can be very helpful in making sure the treatment of Lyme disease and co-infections is focused on your whole body. ND's are trained to take physical imbalances into account as well as making sure your social and emotional lives are balanced and supported. They take more time to get to know their patients and make

treatment plans that encompass the whole patient. They are integrative doctors by nature.

4. **Therapist/Counselor or group support.** Going through a chronic illness like Lyme can take its toll on your mental health. It not only puts you in a chronic stress state, you also have to interface with many doctors and people that say you are making up your symptoms. This can cause anxiety, depression, or feelings of isolation and being crazy. Having a therapist, counselor, or support group in your life can help you reframe the challenges you face when dealing with Lyme. Looking at old conditioning and behaviors that you are carrying from your past can help you clean up boundaries and contracts with people in your life. This brings more balance and awareness to the energy you are using in your daily life.

5. **Massage therapist.** People with Lyme tend to have a lot of pain and stiffness from spirochetes in their tissue and joints. Massage can increase circulation, help balance hormones, relax the mind, and increase healing and recovery times. It allows the body to move into the parasympathetic nervous system instead of the sympathetic nervous system, which increases your healing and calms your mind.

6. **Homeopathic Practitioner.** Homeopathy is a form of Western Medicine that runs on the principle of the Law of Similars—or "like treats like." Instead of treating by opposing someone's symptoms with their opposite, homeopathy treats by matching symptoms from provings of a substance given to a healthy person to the symptoms the ill patient is presenting with. It is well proven and has great results with very few side effects! It falls under nano science as well which is becoming more understood through research and quantum science. I honestly didn't learn about the homeopathic treatment option until much later in my recovery, but I want to encourage you to look into it sooner and to find a homeopathic practitioner

who really tries to find a remedy to treat the core cause of a lot of your health issues which is creating your vulnerability to getting sick in the first place. It is amazing the success I have had in really getting to the cause of my immune system weaknesses that contributed to me getting the infections. Now my vital force is much stronger and balanced, and I need less supplements to maintain my wellness. Look for someone who does classical homeopathy but is open to working with you with Lyme disease and your healing team would be best. See references on my website.

Questions you can ask while interviewing your Healing Team Members:

1. Do you know about Lyme disease?

2. How long have you been working with those with Lyme disease?

3. What is your philosophy on treating Lyme disease?

4. Do you believe I can get better from this?

5. How does your practice work? If I have a problem or a new symptom how do I communicate with you?

6. Do you take insurance? If not, how much will treatment be? Do you have any financial assistance?

7. Are there other specialists you like to work with in treating Lyme disease?

8. Do you know about Chronic Inflammatory Response Syndrome (CIRS) or Mast Cell Activation Syndrome (MCAS)?

9. Do you know about mold illness?

10. Are you integrative? Do you treat with prescriptions or herbs or both?

11. Do you know about gut health and food allergies? Can you help support these areas for me during treatment?

12. Are you comfortable with me working with other practitioners who support my Lyme healing? Would you like to clear them before I see them or do things they suggest?

Building your Personal Support Team:

You also need to build a personal support team for your physical lifestyle needs and changes. This support team is composed of those people in your life that understand or at least support you in making your needed changes to things like diet, exercise, sleep, and environmental exposures.

In our culture there can be a lot of opinions on what is accepted or not around diet. If you don't fit the norms, then you can be seen as a "pain in the rear" or as being "crazy." Having friends and family that have your back and support you in making decisions based on your needs will be crucial not only for your physical health but also your mental and emotional health. If you can't find people who support you in these areas in your daily life then finding a group online that supports you or seeing a counselor or therapist can help with the transitions. Change can scare people around us. This is one reason we see resistance from those closest to us when we start making changes in our lifestyle. If you are changing your lifestyle, then it might change you and you might not like me anymore so you might abandon me.

Suggested Personal Support Team Traits and Members:

- Family.

- Friends.

- Coworkers and bosses.

- People who support your diet needs and encourage you to stick with them.

- Family/Partners who support your sleep habits and lifestyle changes you need to get better.

- Friends/Family who support your exercise goals and needs-maybe a friend or family member wants to commit to going to the gym with you, walking with you, etc. This can help us be more motivated and accountable for our new lifestyle choices until they become habits.

Remember: You may need to set boundaries with those who are not supportive of these changes. These are things that help you get your life back as you heal from Lyme. If that is your goal then you only want people who support and love you on this journey around you.

16

Top 4 Things to Support the Physical Body Healing

In my years helping people with Lyme disease, I have been asked many times, if you could only do 4 things to support the physical body when in treatment for Lyme what would be the most helpful for healing? After really thinking about it and looking at the many things you can do these are the top four I would recommend starting with. You will see positive outcomes if you do them in your daily life.

1. Detoxification Support.

2. Eat low inflammatory organic or non-GMO foods.

3. Exercise Daily - gently and consistently.

4. Avoid and clean up any environmental toxins in your life- - plan to eliminate exposures to blue light, mold, chemicals, perfumes, pesticides, smoke, etc.

In Part III, the next section of this book, I go through each of these things in great detail when we look at blocks in healing. I share more about how you can implement these in your daily life as well. Below is a quick summary of each so you have a quick reference here since it relates directly with healing the physical body.

Top Four Things You Can Do:

1. Detoxification Support

The basic concept here is that if your body becomes too toxic you will get sick and have more symptoms of being sick. Your body will not have as much energy to focus on killing the infections and healing you if it is busy taking out the trash that is overflowing. Your body might need some outside support from you doing exercises at home or by taking supplements to address where you may be deficient.

A few quick tools to help lower your toxic burden and support your body's ability to detoxify:

- Lymphatic system support - walking, dry brushing, swimming, rebounding (bouncing on a trampoline or side of bed).

- Add in elimination support when needed: enemas, saunas and Epsom salt baths.

- Ask your doctors about supplements that support the detoxification pathways (i.e., glutathione and Vit. D and Vit. C, B12, folate and NAC, etc...)

2. Eat organic or non-GMO and low inflammatory foods

This one is pretty self-explanatory. When shopping and eating out try to get foods with labels that say "Non-GMO or Organic" on them. Organic is automatically Non-GMO so if you can't get organic then search for the Non-GMO label and that will be fine.

Studies have shown that genetically modified foods tend to initiate the inflammatory response system in the body, wreak havoc on the immune system, and increase your risk of cancer.

Other inflammatory foods to try to avoid, especially in the start of your treatment, are: sugar, gluten, cow dairy, and for some people plants in the nightshade family.

So when you plan meals think in terms of cooking organic and pasture raised whole foods like grass fed organic meats, organic veggies, and small portions of organic rice. The less processed the better. Add herbs like garlic, turmeric, rosemary, basil, and sea salt that help boost your immune system if you don't have allergies to them.

3. Exercise Daily - gently and consistently

Get gentle exercise daily - brisk walking, gentle swimming, light dancing. Any movement that gets you sweating for even 20 minutes a day. Walking is the best place to start if you haven't been moving much. It's great for lymphatic and circulatory stimulation, which increases oxygen and blood flow to help deliver your treatments more easily. It also helps clear some of the brain fog.

One thing to remember when you have Lyme disease is that you have to be careful to not overdo exercise. It's a balancing act to do just enough to get the movement your body needs but not hit a state of fatigue and Herxing, which takes days to recover from when you have Lyme.

Starting out with 5 minutes of walking a day and working up to 20-30 minutes over a few weeks can be a great way to increase your exercise tolerance. Starting low and working your way up is extremely important in most things you do while treating Lyme disease. Make sure if you crash (get too fatigued) after exercising to not increase your exercise level until you can recover quickly. Then move it up slowly as you get used to the next level. Sometimes I most needed to move when it was the last thing I felt like doing. My doctor told me, "Caroline when you are feeling your worst, that's when you need to get out and walk for 10 minutes. It will help you feel better." And guess what, he was right most the time. It was so hard to force myself to do it but I was always thankful afterwards. I would feel so bad I took Adam or a friend to make sure I didn't have symptoms that would stop me from getting home. So take a friend with you to be safe if you feel bad when you are starting out. Plus, they take your mind off how bad you feel which is always helpful.

Once I was walking for three 15-minute periods a day I graduated to the pool and started swimming. To me swimming was getting in the water and walking, bouncing, and swimming some light laps. I gradually increased my time and distance as long as I could recover from it the same day I did it. I still walked as well. The swimming was great because it allowed me to strengthen muscles without the pain of gravity on my joints. It also helped restore balance between the two sides of my body. We got a pool membership with financial assistance from the YMCA and could use the sauna and steam room too. It became our own little spa treatments for about $25 a month. If I only could swim for 5 minutes some days then that was okay. It didn't cost me anything to leave early.

4. **Avoid and clean up any environmental toxins in your life - plan to eliminate exposures to blue light, mold, chemicals, perfumes, pesticides, smoke...etc.**

If you can decrease the amount of toxins you are exposed to in your living and working environments, you will greatly increase your immune system, decrease inflammation, and internally lower stress throughout your body. Identify what stressors you may be exposed to in your daily life and work to clean them up or switch them out with hypoallergenic materials. More about this in the coming sections.

Doing these 4 things can greatly increase your energy levels each day, and your body's response to the treatments from your healing. I will give you tools and activities you have the power to use in your daily life to help you take control of your healing and how you feel each day. I want to empower you to take responsibility for your body and healing when you can in safe and easy ways.

17

Lifestyle Changes You Can Do to Help Your Physical Body Heal

Sleep

Make sure you are sleeping well through the night. You want to be getting 7-9 hours. If you can fall asleep by 10:00pm at night and sleep until after 6:00am you are doing great.

Identify and Problem Solve Sleep Issues:

Waking up between 1:00am-3:30am may be a sign that you have low blood sugar. Having an easy to eat snack next to your bed can help get your blood sugar back up and you back to sleep faster. I like kind bars or apples with nut butter. You can also try eating a slice of apple with some nut butter on it right before bed and see if it keeps you sleeping through the night. Taking a spoonful of honey before bed can help rebuild your liver's sugar stores and keep you sleeping better through the night. If you have trouble with Candida then skip the honey for now. Talk to your doctor and healing team about this if it is something you are dealing with.

Not being able to fall asleep*:*

1. Make sure the room you sleep in at night has no lights on, especially blue lights. These can be electronic devices that stay lit up even after being closed like TV's, computers, cell

phones, alarm clocks, wall plugs, etc. You can use black tape to cover the lights or unplug them each night. Blue light interrupts the melatonin production in your brain and can keep you up.

2. Take a bath with essential oils that relax you before bedtime if it is hard to unwind. Take a shower if a bath is too long to wash off the day's energy and transition your body for sleep.

3. Turn down lights and do not look at screens for at least a half hour before bedtime.

4. Listen to a mediation, calm soothing music, or something else that helps make you tired. There are some great apps that you can download and use to fall asleep even when your phone is on airplane mode.

5. Use essential oils before bed to relax and calm your mind and body. Lavender and chamomile are two of my favorites.

6. Drink some bedtime tea designed to help you relax and fall asleep.

7. Set a bedtime and make a routine out of it. The body likes sleep to be consistent and having a routine that you stick to can help your body get used to going to sleep at that time.

Diet

Eating low inflammatory foods: Non-GMO or organic. Avoid sugar, gluten, and cow dairy, and try to avoid any allergies you may have. Eat healthy to keep your blood sugar balanced throughout the day. It may mean eating more small meals rather than three big ones a day. If you are not digesting well talk to your doctor about supporting digestion and looking into parasites if you haven't already.

Exercise

Daily moving 5-30 minutes - walking, swimming, etc... Start slow and work your way up. Only move up if you are recovering from the day before.

Supplementing for Deficiencies or Imbalances

This is to be done with the help of your doctor or health care professional. Some areas to check on are the following:

Lymphatic system - does it need any support? Hormonal health imbalances - any support needed? Detoxification system deficiencies? Digestion and gut health? Etc.

Here is a list of basic daily nutrition and activities that can help keep you healthy and balanced:

1. Vitamins, electrolytes, and minerals

2. Eating healthy fats

3. Eating clean proteins

4. Eating complex carbohydrates

5. Getting sunshine or using a light box

6. Earthing - grounding daily - connecting your skin to the earth each day

7. Drinking and bathing in clean water

8. Eating organic or non-GMO foods

18

6 Key Concepts to Know for Supporting Physical Body Healing

Now that you have built your healing and support team and learned 4 of the top things to support your healing in your daily life, we can get to some of the key concepts you need to know to get the help you need. I find if I have a basic understanding of how things work in my body in relation to my treatment I take the treatments better and can ask educated questions when I need help. In this next chapter I will be sharing the *6 Key Concepts for Supporting Physical Body Healing* that are:

Concept #1: Bigger Picture - What Lyme Does to the Body

Concept #2: Circulation - Blood flow and volume are key to healing

Concept #3: Gut Health - the brain and immune system connection to the gut

Concept #4: Inflammation - CIRS and MCA

Concept #5: Detoxification and Lymphatic System Support

Concept #6: Base for Physical Wellness: Nutrition and Supplementation

Concept #1: Bigger Picture - What Lyme Does to the Body

I want to give you a very simplified explanation of what Lyme does after being transmitted to your body so you can make better educated choices to help repair and heal from it. Please remember this is very basic and not completely scientific but an easy to understand concept of what happens.

Lyme disease is caused by the bacteria called Borrelia burgdorferi. It is a spirochete and can drill into the body's tissues and hide from the immune system. This is one reason it can be so hard to treat since diagnosis is usually done through blood and that means the bacteria would need to be in the blood to be seen. If you were infected years prior it may no longer show in the blood because it is living in your tissues. Its spirochete shape allows it to cross through barriers in the body like the brain barrier and allows it to travel to almost anywhere in the body.

According to the CDC Lyme bacteria is transmitted through infected deer tick bites, but some doctors warn it can also be spread through blood transfusions, sexual activity, blood to blood contact, and can even transfer from mother to baby during birth. The main thing to know is if you have Lyme and you have given birth or had sexual activity while infected you may want to have your partner checked even if they have no symptoms. You definitely want a partner that you are sexual with to be tested so you do not get re-infected while in treatment, and to protect them as well. I would recommend using a condom or dental dams while in the treatment process to be safe.

The most common form of transmission is deer ticks, which bite and latch on giving the Lyme bacteria time to be transmitted into the human. Did you know that Lyme is really smart? When the infected tick bites a human and starts sucking in the blood, the Lyme bacteria analyzes the blood and adjusts its physiology to match the hosts blood better. Then the Lyme bacteria transfers itself into the human's blood stream and from there the spirochetes can travel all over the body and make a home in the brain, heart, eyes, joints, etc. It can go everywhere!

When it gets to the tissue it wants to hide in, it drills in and leaves the end of its tail sticking out. The end of the tail secretes enzymes that tell the immune system to turn off because there is no danger. It lowers the immune system's ability to work so it may survive in the host without being found for days, weeks, months, or years. It also likes to take up residence in the thyroid gland, causing the thyroid to become underactive and lowering your basal temperature into the 97 degree range. This is because Lyme turns off a bunch of enzyme activity that your immune system only does in the normal 98 degree range. So it continues to create an ideal living environment inside of the host without being detected by the immune system.

Another thing that happens is some of the Lyme eventually ends up in cyst form. We are not clear on whether the body does this to protect itself or if the Lyme does it to protect itself from getting attacked by the immune system. Cyst form of Lyme hides the Lyme from the immune system and sort of stores it for later. This is one reason traditional treatments of a few weeks of antibiotics don't work to treat Lyme disease and people end up with chronic Lyme. You might feel better temporarily after the antibiotics because it has killed all active Lyme in your body but over time the Lyme hiding in cyst form (aka biofilm) will come out to reproduce and spread.

There is also biofilm that stores biotoxins, the byproducts of the dead Lyme. When your body breaks the biofilm down there is no live Lyme left but the immune system doesn't know the difference and will react to it as though it were a foreign invader. This can give you symptoms of Lyme like fever, inflammation, body aches, nausea, etc. Sometimes near the end of your treatment you may have small flares in Lyme symptoms that end up only lasting a day or two. These usually happen when you are cleaning up biofilm with dead Lyme in them. If your doctor is well versed in Lyme, they will know how to guide you through these stages. I just wanted you to know about it in case you start feeling discouraged when you thought you were through the treatment.

Now this explanation of how Lyme works is to give you a general concept of what Lyme does inside you and why treating and diagnosing can be difficult. Please don't quote me or see any of this as fact. I encourage you to do your own research if it interests you to learn more about how it works in more scientific terms. I found it helpful to understand what was going on inside me from the time I was bitten to when I was diagnosed and started treatment. This way I feel like I can help my medications and supplements work better by imagining them getting into the tissues, finding the spirochetes, and killing them. Or I could imagine blowing up biofilm and my body taking out the dead Lyme easily.

It also made me aware of the fact that I would need to have a doctor who knows about biofilm and how to eradicate it so I could fully heal from the Lyme and its co-infections. I realized it would be important to find supplements and medications that crossed the brain barrier safely and could reach the Lyme in my nervous system.

Remember combining visualizations and believing your medications and supplements are working helps make them work much better. Understanding these basic concepts helps make your mental body stronger in the healing process. I talk more about that when we look at Side 2 of the Diamond of Healing: Mental and Emotional Body.

Concept #2: Circulation - Blood flow and volume are key to healing

It is important to understand the basics of circulation and the function of blood in our health and wellbeing when treating Lyme disease. The basic concepts I want to share are as follows:

- Blood carries nutrients and meds/supplements to your body's structures and organs.

- Blood clears out toxins

- Blood carries oxygen to the body

- Blood delivers immune system defense cells to the body to fight invaders

Blood Circulation is Crucial to Your Healing State

Our blood carries our medications and supplements to our body's tissue for treatment. This means having good circulation is key to your healing. If your circulation is limited or slowed down by inflammation, lack of exercise, dehydration, or scar tissue it will be harder for the body to get the medications your doctor may have you on. The good news is there are things you can do to increase your circulation and make sure your body has the best chance of getting all the meds and supplements you are spending money on.

Another reason it's so crucial to support circulation is that the blood in our body carries out unwanted toxins and bi-products from infections. One of the biggest causes of symptoms while having Lyme disease is when the toxic burden becomes higher. Let's take the metaphor of a bucket that catches all the toxins in our body. When we are healthy our bucket tends to stay half or less full and our body can quickly empty it to start fresh each day. When you are dealing with Lyme disease your bucket fills up quickly and spills over into the body causing a need for even more toxic clean-up. Infections create a lot of biproducts, which are internal toxins, and they can get in the way of your body's normal detoxification systems. So your toxic burden continues to grow while your detoxification system becomes more sluggish. It is crucial to understand that keeping your circulation and hydration up will help your blood flow better and your healing process be much more efficient.

Blood is what carries oxygen to all the tissues and organs in our bodies. The hemoglobin on our red blood cells is where the oxygen binds. Oxygen is crucial for helping immune function and breath. When circulation is lower oxygenation is lowered as well and this causes the body's stress level to decrease immunity responses. This is also one reason a lot of people with Lyme disease find a lot of relief and support through ozone therapy. It increases oxygenation to the entire body helping to fight the infections. It also increases circulation since it thins the blood a little.

Blood circulation also stores, delivers, and transports the white blood cells to the entire body. These are the defense team for the immune system fighting off infections. If your circulation is down or sluggish then your immune system is too. This is another reason it is so important to understand the role circulation plays in healing from Lyme disease.

A few ways to support healthy circulation

- Daily Exercise

- Stretching

- Massage

- Breathing Exercises

Supporting the Quality of the Blood You Are Circulating

So far we have covered increasing and supporting the flow of blood to the body, but what about the quality of the blood that is being moved around? Is the person carrying the nutrients, enzymes, and hormones they need to be healthy? Are these areas depleted from being sick?

When I use the word blood quality I am referring to its volume and density. I am talking about the amount of blood cells in the circulatory system. What is being carried in those cells is the density. The good news is you don't need to know all the scientific specifics to be in support of your healing. I more so want you to have a general concept of blood and why it is so important to support its quality for your treatment and healing. There are some basic things you can do in your daily life to support your blood quality:

1. Making fresh organic berry smoothies that include minerals, electrolytes, proteins, and healthy fats can greatly increase the bio-available nutrients in your blood to be delivered to your body. This will give your body the fuel and the basic essential building blocks to fix itself and heal faster. In the form of a

smoothie, it is also broken down for digestion, and berries have digestive enzymes in them which help those with Lyme who usually have digestive issues anyways.

2. Eating a broad array of colors in your vegetables and eating homemade organic soups can be easier to absorb as well and helps deliver essential nutrients to your body.

Think of baby food - you are helping your body get more out of its food by doing less work digesting it. This allows it to get into your blood quicker and easier. I don't mean eat baby food, I mean think of how much nutrition we stick in a cup of mush for babies. As adults we can do the same with healthy smoothies, homemade whole foods, and some digestive support.

Talk to your doctor about making sure your minerals and electrolytes are covered as well. You may need to add a supplement to rebuild your stores which also helps your blood quality improve. They will know if you need to or not so definitely check with them.

Tools and Ideas Recap

-   Support your circulation each day.

-   Support your blood's quality: volume and density.

-   Smoothies with fresh/frozen organic berries and no added sugar in them. Berries have their own digestive enzymes built into them so you will be able to increase your blood density and volume when you drink them because they are much easier to assimilate.

-   Exercise, especially light cardiovascular exercise, increases circulation and oxygen levels in your blood.

-   Massage increases oxygen delivery to areas of tissue that may otherwise be more blocked when tight.

- Visualize your blood circulating smoothly and easily delivering healthy high-quality blood full of nutrients to your entire body each day. This can greatly aid your body's healing as well.

Concept #3: Gut Health - the brain, immune system connection to the gut

Gut health is important to understand when treating Lyme. You want to support your gut health and repair it as part of your healing journey. Why is gut health so important?

The intestinal lining is the first mechanism of defense for our immune system. It is in charge of most digestive processes including absorbing 90% of the nutrients from the food we eat, after it is broken down in the gut, and then transporting them into our cells.

If this mucosal barrier, the intestinal lining, gets damaged then you begin to have a leaky gut, aka intestinal permeability.

What does it mean to have a leaky gut and why does it matter? When the intestinal lining gets holes in it all the stuff that usually stays inside of our intestinal tract can slip into the body. When this happens the body sees the food particles as foreign invaders and marks them as a danger—this activates the immune system which triggers inflammation and damage to the body in the long run.

When the lining of the intestines is damaged or inflamed malabsorption of vitamins and minerals can take place as well. This makes you more vulnerable to co-infections from food-borne pathogens like parasites and SIBO intestinal bacterial overgrowth. It also raises candida which is an opportunistic species. This is why healing a leaky gut and rebuilding your microbiome are important.

The gut is also directly connected to the brain. The gut is known as the second brain because a lot of our neurological chemicals are made and taken in through the colon. If your gut microbiome is out of balance or you have leaky gut you will usually have cognitive symptoms like brain fog, and memory and focus issues. You might suffer depression and anxiety since about 90% of our serotonin is made and taken in through the colon.

So why is it important to know about how the gut works? If you have the general concept of what is happening you can make choices in your daily life to help your gut health improve or avoid adding things that can make your gut permeability worse. Getting food allergy and intolerance testing done and then avoiding foods you react to will help your intestinal lining have a chance to heal faster. It will bring down inflammation and help your immune system get better. Lowering inflammation and strengthening your immune system are two things that will help your body heal from Lyme disease. I write more about this in the next section of this book, Part III.

Concept #4: Inflammation - CIRS

What is Chronic Inflammatory Response Syndrome (CIRS)?

Chronic Inflammatory Response Syndrome (CIRS) is a multi-system and multi-symptom illness caused by exposure to biotoxins and mycotoxins which come from either your environment, like mold exposures, or from byproducts of infections, which are called biotoxins. What happens is the biotoxins and mycotoxins attach to immune cells and this activates mass inflammation and symptoms all over the body.

Another name for CIRS you might hear is "Mold Illness" because a lot of CIRS cases are triggered by living or working in moldy buildings. Mold toxins are known as mycotoxins. You might ask yourself, but why would someone stay in a building if it's moldy? They ought to know it's moldy? The truth is some of the worst toxic molds are invisible to the eye, and they grow in spots that can't be seen, like below floors or behind walls. They also don't always have a strong moldy smell. So there are a lot of situations where you could be unaware of being exposed.

If you can see or smell mold growing, that is a sign you should get out or fix it! Mycotoxins are being released into the air and you inhaling or ingesting them can lead to a long list of symptoms that make up CIRS. This might not happen overnight since it relies on a buildup of toxins in the body. For those with a genetic predisposition for the "mold gene" once that gene is activated even a 10-minute exposure can trigger a cascade of crippling symptoms, leaving the person feeling horrible. The main concept to take away is, if you are in a moldy building at home or work and treating for Lyme you will want to ask about mold treatment to help your Lyme treatment work better. Please note that chemical exposures, EMF radiation, and internal biotoxins can all also act as triggers, especially once you have active CIRS.

Common symptoms:

- Fatigue

- Inflammation

- Blurred, double, or changed eyesight

- Poor immunity and getting sick more often

- Allergies and sensitivities

- Digestive issues

- Constipation or diarrhea

- Fevers

- Snoring and/or sleep apnea

Cognitive symptoms include:

- Brain fog

- Trouble concentrating

- Mood swings

- Memory loss

- Trouble with executive functioning like planning and scheduling, having almost an ADD effect

- Brain fatigue

Tool Box at home:

- Sign up for the DNRS program online or in person workshops

- Do a ERMI test on your house and work

- Remove all chemical products and replace with non-scented hypoallergenic alternatives

Common misdiagnoses from CIRS:

- Chronic fatigue syndrome and Fibromyalgia

- Anxiety disorders

- Alzheimer's

- Parkinson's Syndrome

- Depression

- Mild Cognitive Impairment

- PTSD

- Somatic disorders

- Lupus

- MS

- Dementia

- Allergic reactions

Concept #5: Detoxification and Lymphatic System Support

The main concept here is that the more toxic you are, the higher your toxic burden is, and the harder it is for your body to treat infections like Lyme disease. Having Lyme and its co-infections increases your toxic burden on its own, especially while you are busy killing the bugs. As you kill the disease it releases biotoxins that cause a lot of die off symptoms that make you feel sicker before you feel better. The more we can help support our detoxification processes in our bodies, the easier it is on our bodies to recover and heal from the treatments. Meaning less intense symptoms and better quality of life. We can also get through treatment faster if the body is under less stress from lowering its toxicity. This also decreases the level of inflammation in the body.

The detoxification and lymphatic systems are important to be aware of to help empower you in your healing journey with Lyme. If your toxic burden is high, your body will focus on detoxification instead of treating the infections. You will feel sick, experience more allergies, and be fatigued with cognitive issues so learning to support your detoxification system can help relieve symptoms and increase the quality of your life while in treatment.

The Lymphatic system's main function is to take toxins out of the blood, filter it, kill infections, and maintain fluid balance in the body. It is a passive system which means it needs to be pumped manually by gentle movement each day. If you are active and moving around that tends to keep it moving but when we get sick we also tend to become less active and the lymphatic system can become more stagnant. It is easy to fix though if you know it's something you need to support. All you have to do is make sure you are walking a few times a day (for example take 2-3 short 10-15 minute walks a day). You can also add swimming, lightly bouncing on a trampoline, or bouncing very lightly on the edge of your bed. These gentle bouncing movements naturally stimulate our lymphatic system helping it take out the toxins from our blood stream. Making sure you stay hydrated by drinking clean filtered water and doing breathing exercises helps pump the lymphatic system as well.

Tools and Ideas to support it:

- Walking for 5-30 minutes a day (work up slowly to 30 min if you are pretty deconditioned)

- Gentle rebounding on a trampoline to pump the lymphatic system, should not become cardiovascular exercise

- Gentle massage - lymphatic drainage massage

- Dry brushing before a shower

- Swimming - the pressure of the water on your body is perfect lymphatic system stimulation. Just bouncing gently in the water is great lymphatic exercise

- Drinking lots of water and fresh juices can help it flow better

Concept #6: Reducing Stress in Your Life is Important to Healing

The basic concept I want you to get around stress is this: When do we do the most repair work? When we are sleeping! That is when we heal. What is the closest thing to sleep while being awake? Being in a state of peace and balance, rest when we are awake. If we find ways to lower stress in our lives, we will heal faster and not just when we are sleeping at night!

Acute or chronic stress tells the body to release higher levels of catabolic chemicals like cortisol which breaks down the body instead of building it up. DHEA is a chemical the body uses to counter the negative effects of high cortisol and this is used while we are in a state of rest. We need rest to rebuild our stores of DHEA and do the clean-up work from the stress caused by fighting Lyme disease on top of everyday life.

The more you can do to identify and reduce stress in your daily life the more it will help you heal faster and regain more of your energy sooner.

Journal Activity

Identify and come up with ways to reduce physical stressors in your life.

- Physical stressors: Chronic Infections, injuries, etc.

- Emotional stressors

- Social stressors

- Crisis/trauma stressors

- Financial stress, especially around treatment costs

Ideas to help you get the support you need for less cost

1. Getting a gym membership where they have a pool, sauna, and/ or steam room can give you a host of tools to help cover a lot of areas in this book. You can take stretching classes to support your lymphatic and muscular system, and swim and bounce in the water for lymphatic drainage support and cardiovascular exercise that's less painful on an inflamed body. You can support your detox system by sweating in the sauna or steam room. One membership can act as a base for covering most of the areas of support your body needs to heal from Lyme disease and other chronic illnesses.

    Most gyms have financial help or can be of assistance depending on your case. YMCAs, for example, have great plans available for those in lower income brackets or needing help due to disabilities or health challenges. Don't be afraid to ask, the worst that can happen is they say no, and you are right where you already were. Don't get discouraged. Try another gym in your area.

2. Enemas at home. An enema kit costs anywhere from $15-$30 and can be bought over the counter in most drug stores or online. This kit is then reused for at least 6 months if you keep it clean and well maintained. This can greatly decrease the amount of money you would otherwise have to pay for colonics ($80-$100 a session usually) as well as on supplements and medications that don't work well when your colon is full of sludge.

3. Epsom salt baths are cheap and very helpful with detoxification, pain relief, and relaxing.

4. Buy yourself a juicer and a blender. A lot of people have these and no longer use them - you could ask friends and family if they have one that they no longer want as well.

5. Health insurance? Medicaid? Etc. Ask about financial assistance at medical offices you go to.

PART II
SIDE 2 OF THE DIAMOND

Mental and Emotional Body

"There was a new voice which you slowly recognized as your own, that kept you company as you strode deeper and deeper into the world."

- Mary Oliver

19

Side 2: Mental and Emotional Body

"I can't change the direction of the wind,
but I can adjust my sails to always reach my destination."

-Jimmy Dean

The second side of the diamond is the mental and emotional body. I found that it was very important to identify how my thoughts and emotions were affecting my current healing and life. I learned new tools that really helped me shift my thoughts and emotions to more healing states allowing me to heal faster. This section introduces some of the things I found important to be aware of throughout my healing journey from Lyme. Please know there is much more I could share on this topic, but I am keeping it shorter here and one of the books I will be publishing later on will focus on the emotional, mental, and psychological challenges of healing from Lyme. I hope this can get you started. Enjoy!

Cognitive Behavior Therapy (CBT) Model in Relation to Healing

Choose your thoughts, emotions and behavior by changing the meaning you attach to trigger situations. The Cognitive Behavioral Therapy (CBT) model teaches that if you don't like how you feel you can identify what situation happened that led to the feeling and what meaning you attached to the situation. You can then see how the meaning you attached to "X" caused an emotional response and the behavior we based on the emotion we feel. Simply put the CBT model is:

When "X" situation happens:

1. We attach a meaning

2. There is an emotion that drives action

3. Behavior or action taken

When you are having reactive roller coaster emotions you can figure out what "X" triggered it and what meaning you attached to that thing that happened. And if you don't like how you feel from it you can choose to change the meaning you are attaching to that "X" so you no longer feel bad or controlled by outside circumstances. It empowers you to take some form of control over your feelings. When you are dealing with Lyme disease there will be emotional reactions that you wish you could change. Sometimes you just need to let them play out and leave your system. No judgment from me either way, it's a matter of what feels good to you and your physical body. This is just a tool I wanted to share to help you change your thoughts and emotions to be more healing to your body.

Biochemicals are released by our emotions and thoughts trigger our emotions. These biochemicals can affect your physical health in positive or negative ways depending on whether the emotion triggered is stressful or relaxing to the body. The good news is we have the power to choose and change the meanings we give to situations in our lives. The meaning is the key to what drives the emotions and then behaviors. If you don't like how you feel, change the meaning you are giving to whatever is making you feel that way. Changing the meaning is really about changing how we are thinking about something, changing what we believe to be true or not.

Belief is powerful - believe you can heal and you can. Prayer and visualization are great tools you can use to help yourself heal through the power of clear, healthy thoughts and beliefs. Belief connects thoughts to your heart's desire or guidance which makes it an even stronger force. Faith falls in this area too. The ultimate goal would be to live from your heart and have your heart direct your thoughts. When we live from our heart it's hard not to find yourself in states of love, joy, acceptance, compassion, forgiveness, empathy, kindness, peace… Grief may come or go but fear and anger don't tend to stem from our heart center --- they come from our gut and mind. If you want to simplify your life and not have to focus on your thoughts --- stay focused on living from your heart first. It will take care of a lot of the lower frequencies that can cause illness or trouble healing. In learning to listen with your heart instead of your mind you will find that you are rarely triggered because you come from a place of understanding, patience and love. You have empathy for other people as fellow humans. It's easier to hear what they are saying without all your thoughts and preconceived notions changing the filters you see the world through. When you practice being in your heart instead of your head you can be more present in the moment and stay connected to spirit, your higher self, and God.

Crazy?!

You may feel crazy after being dismissed by doctors and society for having Lyme. Most people go through more than a few diagnoses before finding out they have Lyme disease or co-infections. These multiple diagnoses and incorrect diagnoses come with a lot of visits to the doctors. Some misunderstanding doctors who tell you there is something wrong with you but it's not physical, it's all in your head. They tell you to go see a psychiatrist or therapist.

The fact is, they probably are right, it is in your head! It's Lyme and its co-infections in your nervous system are messing with your body's chemicals and making you feel terrible! And yes finding a therapist can help too but usually to help support you through the shame and depression that you may face when being told over and over again that there is nothing wrong with you. They may say Lyme doesn't exist, that they can't treat you, or don't know what's wrong with you so they say you are making it up. You probably have heard one or more of these from doctors, family members, or friends. Remember, you are not crazy! You are healing and trying to find your way in a CRAZY SYSTEM. Keep looking for the right doctor to be on your team, and keep people in your life who support and don't shame you. You are dealing with a real infection with real physical, mental, social, emotional, and spiritual challenges. Don't give up!

How Infections Can Play with Your Mind: Understanding the Mental Health Issues When Treating Lyme Disease

I introduced in Part I the concept of infections having frequencies that affect our body. These infections and their frequencies also affect our emotional and mental body causing emotional swings, confusion, neurological issues, and psychological disturbances. A lot of children who have Lyme come down with learning disabilities and disturbances that they did not have before the infection. These symptoms can look like other disorders and might come on suddenly seeming very out of character for the person experiencing them. So here is a look at a few ways they can manifest mentally.

Suicidal Thoughts and Loss of Hope

When Bartonella dies off people report having suicidal thoughts or hearing voices telling them to "give up, what's the point, you are going to die anyway." This is the Bartonella trying to get you to stop the treatment so it can live. It can cause bipolar tendencies and be misdiagnosed as a psychiatric condition. It also is the main culprit as a coinfection with Lyme, causing neurological Lyme disease issues. It also can trigger fear and anxiety. Some are diagnosed with bipolar or depression disorders from Bartonella.

Lyme Rage

Like walking on a minefield, anything and everything can suddenly trigger you to have intense emotional reactions even if it usually didn't matter much to you. The driver in front of you, a person on their phone, or your friend says something and you explode out of nowhere. It's intense and impulsive and can't be stopped. I found I would sometimes be outside of my body watching myself react and thinking, "This is so unlike me, I really don't feel that strongly or angry about this, but I can't stop myself from raging."

Depression and Anxiety can start or increase with Lyme Disease

Bartonella is known to cause bipolar disorder, depression, anxiety and neurological disorders. You can also have depression and anxiety become heightened from imbalanced gut health from pathogens and leaky gut while in treatment for Lyme. The colon produces and absorbs more than 90% of your serotonin each day so if your colon or digestion is not working right the neurochemicals are directly impacted causing depression, anxiety, and low dopamine issues to occur, leading to low motivation too.

Candida overgrowth can cause terrible bouts of brain fog, low motivation, fatigue, and depression as well.

Babesia, the *malaria of North America*, can cause anxiety and depression in a lot of people. It is a parasite of the red blood cells that lowers your iron and oxygen levels. This leaves you with anemia and less dopamine, which can bring on depression or low motivation and symptoms of anxiety, fatigue, and shortness of breath.

Parasites, when being treated and dying, can cause feelings of anger, neediness, despair, loss of hope, irritability, lack of focus, confusion about your life, and fatigue with low motivation or life force. When treating parasites, it is usually a good time to re-write contracts with people, setting boundaries and rebalancing energy between those you interact with.

Words Matter

*"Find someone whose thymus gland tests weak and say to him,
"I love you." His thymus will test strong. We are only beginning to
learn through Behavioral Kinesiology of the tremendous power of
words, either to help or to harm others."*

- John Diamond, M.D. (p. 109, Your Body Doesn't Lie)

Choosing your words matters when speaking about your health, healing, Lyme disease, and other illnesses you have. The power of your words can either greatly help you heal or hurt you. Owning things brings more energy to whatever you are owning so choosing phrases that don't make the illness part of your identity can help you heal quicker or let go of the challenge. An example of this concept is the use of "MY" Lyme vs. "the" Lyme, or "I am so tired of" … "I'm sick of" … These are bringing energy into your life through ownership which your subconscious hears and can believe it to be true. It's one way we can accidentally end up self-sabotaging our intended healing. One step forward, two steps back. This concept is the base for hypnosis in a way. You are speaking to the subconscious mind that runs the show in the background which is why it can work so well to speed up healing too.

Start being aware of what language you naturally use when speaking about your health and how you are doing. Does it resonate with what you are trying to do, like *heal*, or does it resonate with staying sick as an identity? I find when I use the word "my" in front of an illness I am owning it and attaching it to part of my identity whereas if I just say *the* Lyme disease --- it keeps my identity away from the Lyme. Instead, I am experiencing Lyme, but it is not defining who I am as a soul or human. It's a temporary experience. This gives me more power to treat it and let it go because it is not a permanent part of me.

Environment Matters

Choosing the environment you surround yourself with matters. "You become who you spend your time with" is a saying I heard growing up.

I finally get it much more now that I have had Lyme. I became more sensitive to energy and people I was around. Make sure while you are healing from Lyme that you choose to spend your time around those people that bring you joy, love, and optimism and allow you to be you as you are. It's so important to not have to put on a show when you are healing. You want all your extra energy going into healing instead of worrying about trying to control what others think of you. The truth is you can't! It's absolutely none of your business what others think of you and that is the truth! Be yourself!

Emotions Matter

Emotions carry their own frequencies. Joy, love, hope, compassion, gratitude, and forgiveness are all emotions that help raise our spirits, our vibe, and our frequency! Emotions like grief, anger, frustration, hopelessness, and fear are all examples of emotions that lower frequency vibes, causing us to go into stress states. I am not saying it is bad to have these, its human to experience all of them. It can help us release and let go of trauma stored in our bodies from being hurt-feeling, grief, or having a boundary crossed, etc. The key is to be aware of which emotional states you spend more time in than others each day. If they raise your vibration you will be in more of a healing state - able to recover faster. If they are in the lower frequencies then make sure you are finding ways to shift yourself out of those states once you have processed the emotion so you're better able to live in wellness.

Emotions trigger the release of different bio-chemicals in our body - some are helpful in healing, others can make us worse. Bio-chemicals in the body either turn your healing and growth on or off, leading towards death. Simply explained, we want to learn to turn the healing chemicals on for good health and turn off the bad ones. When do we do the most healing? While we are asleep --- while we are at rest. So, lowering your stress through lifestyle changes, changing the meaning of your triggers, and other practices can greatly increase our good emotions which release chemicals for our body to heal more easily.

Toolbox for Supporting Releasing and Healing of Stored Emotions and Trauma:

1. Therapy: Find a therapist who knows about post-traumatic stress disorder (PTSD) and Lyme or chronic illness stresses. You could investigate Cognitive Behavioral Therapy (CBT) or other modalities.

2. Try out RESET Meditation which can help clear unconscious emotional patterns and blocks: https://www.kiaorafox.com

3. "When you choose Reset Meditation, you are choosing to transform yourself, to mature and grow. It is 100% your process and your opening! Reset Meditation helps the client to reclaim mental, emotional, and physical balance as well as a sweet opening to the soul, which is the true YOU. If you want real change, Poly Vagal Nerve work and Polarity Neutralization will get you there!"

4. Hypnosis for healing: find a hypnotherapist who can work with you to design hypnosis to help you heal or release emotional blocks or triggers.

5. Make a timeline of your life or illness, talk to your younger self, and integrate your younger self to your current self and future self.

6. Create art or journal.

20

Power of the Mind to Heal

*"If my mind can conceive it, if my heart can believe it,
then I can achieve it."*

- Muhammad Ali

One of the big tools I learned to use on myself while in treatment for the Lyme was Self-Hypnosis and visualizations. It is a surprisingly easy thing to do. The overall concept is that you come up with images or cartoons that help you heal from whatever it is that is bothering you. Let me share an example to make more sense of this.

One of my favorite things to do is to get in hot water like a hot tub, bath, or hot spring to go into a healing trance state. I had just learned about doing Self-Hypnosis from my therapist, John, so I decided I would try it out while at a hot spring for the weekend. I submerged myself in the hot water until my head was floating with my ears just under the water but my mouth above so I could continue to breath easily. While underwater you can hear your breath much louder than when you are out of it. I find that hearing my breath in a calm rhythm helps me get into a trance state faster. I close my eyes and breath and then I start seeing the visualization of cowboys lassoing all the Lyme spirochetes in my body and taking them out gently. The cowboys are riding on horses and finding all the Lyme spirochetes with ease. I start smiling while I imagine them working their way through my brain, my back, my organs and the rest of my body cleaning house. I see beautiful sunshine and white filling the space where the spirochetes used to be as the cowboys take them away. I thank the cowboys and I tell the Lyme it is no longer welcome inside my body. Remove itself or it will be killed and taken out quickly. Be gone. I would do this for 10-30 minute sessions, a few times a day. This is one example of the type of visualizations you can try out. The great thing is your imagination is the limit so have fun being as creative as you want! The key is making yourself smile or laugh when you visualize it happening. Making healing fun is so important! That way you will want to do it and your body will respond to it with open arms!

Make time for Mini Retreats and Fun in your Daily Life

Another thing that really helped my mental and emotional body heal was coming up with small day trips or activities that my partner Adam and I could do each week. Having fun allows us to play and be creative, which are two things that help bring more joy, love, and hope into our lives. It is a way to give yourself a break from the daily routine of feeling sick at home or work. It can help you change your perspective on life and allows you to connect to things that spark your souls desire to experience new things. These little outings do not need to cost much or take a lot of energy. You are in charge of creating them. Going to sit in nature and having a favorite meal packed as a picnic with someone you enjoy spending time with can do it. Go to a movie, a game room, a museum, or to do a tourist activity in your town. You could go to a local hot spring or spa for a half day or go out for a meal at a special restaurant. It's about changing it up and doing something that excites you to keep your energy fresh and your spirits up so you heal quicker.

For me it was going to hot springs near us in California for day trips. Heat really helps me. Adam and I would drive to the hot springs every Saturday and stay all day because I found floating in the hot water would allow me to quiet all the chatter and distractions of everyday living and hear myself. Adam and I would read books, talk, and take naps on the lounge chairs. We'd go into town and eat some great food while walking around being tourists each visit. It would feel like we went on a week-long trip by the time we went home that night even though it had only been the day. We would laugh a ton and disconnect from screens and the worries of our home life that can take over our free time. We also got zoo memberships and started going once a week to walk around to get exercise and feel like we were on a trip. We didn't stop at all the animal sites but went to exercise and walk like we were on a safari. That membership was worth it since it motivated me to walk and gave us a quick getaway without having to leave town.

Meditation is another way people go into this healing trance state. Massage and body work can also help as well as exercise, heat, listening to relaxing music, or even silence.

During warm baths at my house I go into a deep healing trance state. If I talk to my body and tell it that it is healing when in this state I actually start healing and feel much better that day than I would if I didn't do it. I also found the reverse to be true. One time I decided to do the opposite to see what happened. I told myself I wasn't healing, that I had Lyme, I was very sick, and I should just give up. The amazing thing that happened was all of it came true and not just for me inside but on the outside. People kept commenting that I didn't look well all day, asking if I was okay. I felt actual anxiety and fear about my survival at a core level. It ended up taking me a week or two to recover from it. The power of our thoughts, words, and beliefs, especially when in a trance state, is much stronger than we consciously realize. If we tell our body we don't like it or it is bad it will take a physical toll on our health. If we tell our body it is well, healing, and beautiful your physical body will respond with healing and strength. Our minds are very powerful in both healing and harming ourselves. The key is making sure your intention is positive for healing. I have never tried to think negatively about my body again because I was so surprised how long it took to rebound even with doing the same things to return to a healing state.

Imagine the power of a doctor who we put our trust into, and then they tell you that "you won't get better", "you're terminal", "there is nothing I can do so live with it and get used to it", or "you're crazy, it's all in your head." The power of language and the energy it brings with it can greatly affect our energy body and in turn our physical body. Doctors are trying their best to help but some don't realize how much power they have with the words they choose to use with their patients. If they did they would be much more careful about what they focused on and how they said it. The truth is no one really knows what will happen from one moment to the next. Why not focus on the healing outcome? Warn the patient of the odds but focus on the light. It can make all the difference in their recovery or not. If you are aware of this you can be less passive and speak up to people who say scary things about your outcome and you can own what you know to be true --- that everyone can heal, anything is possible, and the person speaking just isn't aware of this truth.

Empower yourself and don't let anyone shift your frequency into one of fear to get you to do what they want you to. You are the only driver of your ship and no one else can do it for you. You can ask for an amazing crew and make your best decisions for you on your path, the rest is up to God.

Positivity Heals

Think positive, you are who you hang out with and what you spend time on. Friends, coworkers, family, music, films, TV, conversations, focuses… These are the things that can affect our lives, moods, behaviors, and physical health more than you realize.

When you are dealing with chronic health challenges like Lyme, you're in a chronic stress state. Your adrenal glands work overtime trying to lower inflammation in the body to fight for your life. This makes you more vulnerable than normal to energies around you because your adrenals are key to your ability to stay grounded and to have boundaries. People who have burned out adrenal glands are too tired to even decide whether they need to have a boundary with the outside world or not and this ends up causing even more stress on their bodies.

Eventually they hide out at home away from people because they can't keep their boundaries clear and are exhausted.

When cortisol is low your auric boundary is weakened and sometime non-existent. It can make you very vulnerable to outside influences and energies of others near you.

The best advice a doctor gave me while I was at my lowest low of my treatment was to only allow myself to be around positivity—positive people, positive movies, TV shows, music... They encouraged me to laugh and find comedies as much as I could. Laughter allows the adrenals to recharge themselves and release stress. Some studies have shown that people with adrenal fatigue have gotten better just by laughing as much as possible and taking high levels of vitamin C. It was such a simple solution. I had nothing to lose but letting go of some anxiety inducing action movies and cutting a few people out of my life who were energy vampires.

Tools:

1. Hypnosis --- find, or have made, hypnosis for healing recordings.

2. Make and use Affirmations for your healing.

3. Listen to a guided meditation for grounding, clearing, and connecting to your higher self.

4. Chakra Meditation to help clear and align your chakras.

5. Here is your *"Positivity Prescription" sheet*: For the next day, week, or month only watch shows that are positive, calming, humorous, and non-surprising. Promote your parasympathetic nervous system, not sympathetic nervous system! Heal your adrenal glands faster.

PART II
SIDE 3 OF THE DIAMOND

Social Body

21

Side 3: Social Body

"One of the lessons that I grew up with was to always stay true to yourself and never let what somebody else says distract you from your goals."

-Michelle Obama

The focus of this side of the diamond of healing is balancing and identifying your social needs. Humans are social beings. Our survival once depended on community, tribes, and power in groups. We are programmed to need others because without them we would not have survived on our own in nature. Humans are mammals that need their parents to survive until their young adult years. Because it is such an integral part of our survival it is connected to our physical needs through reward chemicals when we engage with others.

When you have a chronic illness like Lyme disease you can become isolated or anti-social for many reasons. You may feel too fatigued or ill to see people. It might be too draining or you may be embarrassed to show up in the state you are in, too vulnerable. Another reason may be that you feel like an outcast because the culture has made people with Lyme out to be crazy or making it up. So there is a social tag you wear when you are open about having Lyme and that can isolate you in our uneducated culture. The good news is the stigma has been getting much better in the last few years but it still is there! You might also get told that you can't have Lyme because it's only on the east coast. These falsehoods that persist in mainstream medicine add to the stress of trying to come out and be social while struggling with the challenges that Lyme brings.

Another obstacle that I see a lot in those who have Lyme is energy crashes in the afternoon and evening. They can no longer stay up late to socialize, go to parties, or bars for dancing. Even dinner invites may be too late at night for them to push though adrenal fatigue. As much as you want to see friends like you used to, the reality is that recovery from one night out can take days or weeks. You start to avoid anything that drains you like that. Becoming more house bound and less social can lead to its own set of anxiety and depression symptoms. This is why I wanted to address the "social body" on the diamond of healing.

So what are things to consider when assessing the balance and health of your social body?

1. How often do you go out each week?

2. Who do you see? Make a list of the most frequent interactions you have and who are they most commonly with?

   - Doctors?

   - Support team members?

   - Friends - who?

   - Family?

   - Church or Community Support groups in some way?

3. What do you do when you go out?

   - Grocery shop - see people regularly in community?

   - Spiritual community: Church, temple, etc?

   - Exercise: Can you meet others to do it? Can you go to a gym where you see familiar faces each time?

   - Take Classes?

   - Work?

   - Go to School?

4. Who do you live with?

   - Partner?

   - Spouse?

   - Friends?

   - Roommates/Housemates?

   - Family?

5. What did you do for fun this week?

   - Every week you want to make sure you are scheduling at least 1 fun thing FOR YOU. We need to play and have joy in our lives. Joy can inspire, motivate, and spark creativity, which are all things that can help you go into a healing state faster! You will have more energy when you're having fun!

6. What brings you joy? What are your passions?

7. If you are finding that you are not interacting much with others in your daily life then plan a few outings in your week to get you out of your house and in society. Going out helps neurological function by bringing stimulation of sound, sight, smell, touch, and speech to the brain. It exercises the neurons and keeps them firing and healthy. The more isolated you become the greater the effect going out can become. Over time this can make neurological and cognitive symptoms even worse. See your outings and socialization as a form of free physical therapy for your brain and body.

8. 8) How do you feel after spending time with _____? With the _____ group? Are you more energized or more drained after being with them?

Social Support

On the physical body side of the diamond, I focused on building your medical support team - Your Healing Team. You also need to build a social support team. People in your daily life that support you and you can have positive interactions with each week. So who in your life is a positive support in your Lyme treatment and healing?

- Friends? Name them. Are they a positive influence?

- Family members who support your health needs and who you are in a positive way? Name them.

- Co-workers? Your boss? Do you have support for your challenges at work? Do you hide it? Is it an issue?

Introvert verses Extrovert Social Needs

You'll want to recognize if you are more introverted, extroverted or somewhere in the middle. If you don't know and want to learn more, I suggest taking a quick online questionnaire to see where you score on the spectrum.

When I use introvert or extrovert I am talking about how you recharge. Do you recharge your energy by being by yourself? Do you need alone time to better know who you are? Or are you someone who likes to be around people and feels recharged after spending time with others? It is a misconception that introverted means shy and extroverted means outgoing. Being shy has more to do with how much shame someone has than how they recharge. Introverts tend to carry more shame because they are told that there is something wrong with them for wanting to be alone or for liking reading instead of going out with friends as a kid, for example. So you might see more introverts being shy and having shame in social situations because they tend to be misunderstood and pressured to be someone they aren't. There are also a lot of empowered and outgoing introverts, one in the public eye is Whoopi Goldberg. She is introverted and recharges by being on her own, but when needing to be in front of audiences and interact with others for her work she is outgoing, loud, and fun. It does not change how she recharges though. She has to go home and be with herself to stay recharged and not get sick.

If we do not recharge our energy, our battery becomes out of balance and we will get sick physically.

On average 80% of the population is naturally more extroverted but even if you are introverted you still need connections to others in society to be healthy, just less time doing it.

Communicating with Friends and Family Expectations and Contracts

Lyme disease makes it hard to predict daily whether you will have a "good or bad" day until the actual day starts. One challenge this creates is that it can feel hard to plan for the week ahead because you don't want to commit to things you may have to pull out of. This tends to be a big social no-no and seen as inconsiderate of others and their time. You may even start to avoid making plans so you don't end up upsetting others you care about. Instead, if you can, communicate that you may need to change or reduce plans based on what is going on as part of your treatment for Lyme. Assure them that in the future you hope to be back to normal.

This is important to share with people in your life because otherwise you can be judged as flaky, inconsistent, or trying to hurt the other person. The truth is you just have to take care of yourself if you are going to get better.

Letting friends and family know what types of challenges you are going through can really help lower the amount of stress you experience with people who feel disappointed by last minute change of plans.

This also will take the stress off you when you make plans, knowing that if you wake up feeling too bad to meet up you won't be judged for rescheduling. This alone sometimes makes the difference in being able to go out or not. You may want to add that you might need to leave early if you go to do something with them. Symptoms from Lyme can hit suddenly and wipe us out. You need to know it is safe to leave a situation without making a big scene or drama. This will greatly increase your social health and wellbeing, contributing positively to your overall healing and wellness.

Identifying and Solving Some of the Challenges in Relationships for Those with Lyme

Lyme sometimes forces us to change our initial relationship contracts with others. If you were the caretaker when you got together and now you need care taking—you are breaking the contract from when you chose each other as partners. Being aware of this allows for direct communication about the change and avoids passive aggressive behaviors used to punish the other person. Remember that the end goal would be to aim at growing together and becoming more balanced in partnership roles in the long run. The person who used to be cared for needs to grow up and take on some of the responsibility and learn to take care of and give more to their partner. While the person who was the caretaker before getting Lyme must grow by learning to ask for help and accepting care and support from their partner. When you heal more fully this will hopefully rebalance in a healthy way of being present for each other, both giving and taking when needed. Taking responsibility for your stuff and vice versa.

It can feel unfamiliar to take on new roles depending on the roles we saw growing up in our families. As humans we naturally want to go to what is familiar because even if it's not balanced or healthy, it feels safer in the moment since we know what to expect. This is the healing work you do with the people close to you in your life when you get Lyme disease. It forces you out of your comfort zone of being self-reliant and makes you able to spot where you need to show your vulnerability as a human and allow someone else to give you support. This is part of the social side of healing.

This changing of the original contracts between you and your part-ner can lead to a "teeter-totter" effect as you heal. When I was heal-ing from Lyme, I noticed something interesting happen between my husband and I. As I got better, my husband got sick or had a crash or trouble. It was like as I got better, he got worse. It was completely unintentional but noticeable enough for both of us to catch it with the help of our therapist.

It was in essence a teeter-totter because as he got sick when I was getting better, I was forced back into the caretaker role fulltime. Then I would crash and he would get better to take care of me. We didn't know how to be with each other without having one of us playing the role of caretaker and it meant rewriting our contract to be partners and not needing to play the role of one down and one up to know our role.

We went through this for about a year before recognizing it was happening. Once we identified and worked on it with our therapist, we were able to stop the teeter-tottering by talking about it before we unconsciously did it to each other. This may be something to look at in relating with your partner as you get better and can do more and more on your own. If you notice this, or another, phenomenon going on you can have a conversation about it and make it something interesting to look at together --- not blaming either of you for doing something wrong, instead being curious about the pattern, why it is happening, and what you both can do to help stop it.

Finding Social Connection Through Community Interactions

Where do you see yourself contributing to others? Connecting with others? We all need purpose in our lives. Sometimes it may just be by being present for a friend or family member. That's it. For others it may be their career; reaching people through a passion or work. We all affect others we meet in our daily life. What is your purpose when it comes to interacting with others in the world?

I went from teaching kids to doing one-on-one counseling to literally only being able to get myself out of the house three times a week. But in those three times a week I intentionally made a plan to meet up and see one person who I could give my attention to and share love with. That was enough. I had purpose and connection that fed my social body. However, it's easy for me to be alone because I am extremely introverted and when I was sick with Lyme, I needed even more alone time to focus inward and recharge. Quiet to heal.

Now if I were extroverted it would have been more important for me to add some sort of social interaction each day to stay fulfilled and heal. If interaction is what recharges me, then I need it more than just a few times a week to have the energy to heal. Maybe I would make plans each day to have a friend or family member come to my house while I did some of my healing activities. Coming up with ways to add socialization while still meeting your health needs when extroverted can really help you feel more optimistic and energized about treatments. Finding *your* "people" who understand and support *your* needs while you are going through treatment will help greatly. Seeing them earlier in the day tends to work out better than the old social evenings, due to adrenal fatigue in most cases of Lyme. Communicating that to them can help them understand.

Another way to connect in our current society is through online support or common interest groups. You could explore those options if it is hard for you to get out or you worry about your immune system being lower with the COVID-19 pandemic going on or something else like that. You can even take a class online that requires connecting to other students in a controlled setting, which can feel less overwhelming if you aren't up for going out to meet people. What's great about taking classes for fun is that you are with a group of others who share some sort of common interest with you since they signed up for it as well. Check out local, state, federal, and private grants for classes you are interested in. There are a surprisingly diverse amount of grants available.

It can be fun to experiment with new ways to be social that you may never have done without the push from your health challenges. So make it fun and grow in your communication and vulnerability around social needs to help balance your body in the process.

PART II
SIDE 4 OF THE DIAMOND

Spirit Body

Invitation

by Mary Oliver

Oh do you have time
to linger
for just a little while
out of your busy

and very important day
for the goldfinches
that have gathered
in a field of thistles

for a musical battle,
to see who can sing
the highest note,
or the lowest,
or the most expressive of mirth,
or the most tender?
Their strong, blunt beaks
drink the air

as they strive
melodiously
not for your sake
and not for mine

and not for the sake of winning
but for sheer delight and gratitude
believe us, they say,
it is a serious thing

just to be alive
on this fresh morning
in the broken world.
I beg of you,

do not walk by
without pausing
to attend to this
rather ridiculous performance.

It could mean something.
It could mean everything.
It could be what Rilke meant, when he wrote:
You must change your life.

22

Side 4: Spirit Body

*"Re-examine all that you have been told...
dismiss that which insults your soul."*

-Walt Whitman

And now we come to the last side of the diamond of healing, *Side 4: Spirit Body*. So far we have covered the physical body, the mental/ emotional body, and the social body. You have learned specific things you can do to support physical healing and things to consider when working with your doctors. We have seen how emotional health and how your thoughts and beliefs can put you in a healing state or even make you worse. You have learned about building a support system with others in society as a way to have purpose and connection, which all humans need to stay alive. Now we are adding the spiritual body. This is something very unique and special for each individual as well. As part of your Lyme journey, you will get to define and refine more of what your spiritual beliefs are and what it looks like in your daily life. Without looking at this side you would be missing a lot of growth that can come from going through bigger challenges like Lyme. It helps complete whole body healing and balancing. So, let's get started.

Are you connected to your higher self? Can you hear yourself? This part of you is what connects to God, the higher power, the universe or source, whatever you want to call it.

Being connected to our spiritual body helps bring a bigger perspective of gratitude in life, especially during challenging times. It enables us to step back and see ourselves and our troubles with curiosity and gratitude in terms of what we might be learning in the moment. I found that if I was healthy and balanced in my spiritual body then I had a much easier time connecting to the bigger picture and finding peace in the chaos, hope in the pain, and gratitude for all that was going on around me even if it wasn't something I wanted to be dealing with. I can better understand that my situation is just a stone in my path of life and I will get past it.

If I am not connected to my core, my spirit, then I have a lot more difficulty getting through the hard times. I feel more like a victim, more emotionally reactive, frustrated, angry, and exhausted. I want to give up hope, throw in the towel, or sometimes I even wish it would all just be over, including my life. When I hear thoughts like that coming through it is a huge red flag to become more aware and start implementing some of the tools I know help me reconnect to myself.

I know when I am healthy and spiritually balanced I am very excited to be alive in this human body right now. I have a lot more experiences and life in me to live. So those types of dramatic thoughts are not me, they are not me connected to my whole self. Those are thoughts from an exhausted emotional and ungrounded Caroline. I really don't want her running the show for long. Sometimes she needs a few minutes in the spotlight to melt down but it's much nicer if I am connected to spirit and don't even go there. It's way less stress on my body.

I also find that my sense of humor is much better when I am connected to my core. Because I can see the bigger picture I am better able to laugh or find some sort of humor in a situation. Laughter is so healing! It literally heals the adrenal glands and helps restore them. Laughter is light and keeps us feeling better even about the most difficult situations. Sometimes in meditations I like to watch myself like I'm in a movie and I can see all the things I am getting emotional about and I tend to find humor in it. It can be another gift from spirit perspective.

*"You have to be spiritual in order to truly be able
to accept what the world is about."*

- Mary Oliver

It is also important to this side of the diamond to find what your purpose is. Living in alignment with who you are, what your soul wants to be doing and walking your path will help you heal faster. Having something you look forward to or can work on a little bit each day can make a huge difference in your health: physical, emotional, mental, social, and energetic! The key is to really think about what is important to you while you are connected to your core self. Listen to your authentic self. Your spirit is a guide.

When you are in alignment with your Purpose and Spirit-God you may find that:

- Things that you need for your health and living are easily provided to you.

- You have more coincidences or God moments.

- You feel stronger physically and more grounded.

- You are more confident.

- You are more optimistic.

- You are better able to live in the moment and find gratitude.

- You have more energy.

- You can better be who you are while around other people who may not be at the same frequency as you. Or you are aware enough to choose to remove yourself from toxic emotional, social, or physical environments.

- You will feel less triggered and more emotionally even keeled. It's harder to rock your boat.

- You might have a better sense of humor about life and be able to see yourself in a positive light.

- Going to church, a spiritual group, or interest groups that are in alignment with who you are at your core increases your life force/spirit helping you connect to your higher power/God more easily.

- Assessing if the group is spiritually healthy for you or not. Are they non judging? Accepting? Do you feel better after being around them or worse?

"A walk in nature walks the soul back home."

-Mary Davis

Building a Spiritual Practice

Sometimes adding spiritual activities to your daily routine helps keep up on the spiritual house cleaning. In other words it keeps you more connected and helps you realize when you are out of balance so you can get back on track faster. Your connection to your spirit is sort of like muscle memory in your body - the more you do it, the easier it is to jump back into it if you go off track.

What is a spiritual practice?

Having a spiritual practice to me is having a routine of making time to do things that connect me to my higher self or spirit. It is different for each of us so I encourage you to think about what works best for you and your schedule. You want to pick things you can and will do so you are successful at incorporating it into your daily life even when it gets busy. Going out in nature, even for a short visit, can be a great way to quickly connect spiritually. Activities like watching a sunset or sunrise, taking a quick walk on a trail near trees, or spending time near a natural water body like a lake or ocean. See below for more ideas.

A List of Ideas and Activities to Strengthen Your Spiritual Body

-   Going to church, temple, or spiritual service of some sort with a community of people at a certain time each week.

-   Meditating for 10-30 minutes each morning before your day gets going. You can choose what type of meditation, i.e. silent stillness, breathing exercises, or a guided meditation. The goal is to connect you to you, to God, to your spirit, and to a higher power. You should feel energized or peaceful from this, not drained or exhausted.

-   Reading a message each day from a spiritual book --- i.e. the bible, a spiritual teachings book, or drawing a card in the morning. Something that helps you look at the day introspectively and helps make you aware of the growing bigger picture.

-   Being of service to others by doing something nice for someone else without them knowing or volunteering to help somewhere. Something kind to help someone else from your heart.

-   Keep a gratitude journal, express gratitude at mealtime, send gratitude to those in your life through a card, text, email, or in person.

-   Praying for others, yourself, for help, for guidance…

-   Lighting candles at dinner in honor of someone or something that means something to you spiritually. Taking a moment of silence to think of all those you love and those who love you as you look at the flame.

-   Saying sorry and taking responsibility when you make a mistake or hurt someone. We all lose our cool sometimes. Owning that we are not perfect and asking for forgiveness and practicing forgiveness with others in our lives can be part of a spiritual practice.

-   Practicing Self-Care when we are exhausted is a spiritual practice because, when I take care of myself, I find I tend to slow down from the fast pace of life, become more relaxed, and open up to hear my spirit. Taking a bubble bath, a nice shower, cutting my nails, washing my body, and doing those type of things can become a spiritual practice because it allows us to tune in to our inner self and hear better.

- Going outside in nature. Going for a walk, a bike ride, fishing, camping, etc. Something as simple as sitting in the backyard on the grass near a tree. Connecting with nature with the intent of just being still in nature is a great way to connect to your spirit and heal yourself a lot of the time.

Now you do not need to do all of these by any means. You could pick one or a few you like or anything else that works for you. Just make sure you have something each day that allows you to connect and raise your frequency. You might think "I am too busy to do that today" but what I find is I am way more efficient and effective with my other areas of my life if I am in touch with my spirit and connected to the bigger picture. Right after waking up can be a great time to jump on it with a quick meditation with my higher self or God. It also becomes way more exciting and fun to do the work during the day if I have started out feeling connected. When you are dealing with Lyme it can be even more important to stay connected to your higher self because it helps give you energy and uplifts you through life's challenges.

Building your Spiritual Support System

You are looking for someone or a group of people that you feel raises your spirit after you are with them.

- Do you feel brighter or lighter after being with _____?

- Do you feel warm and optimistic or calm and at peace after seeing _____?

These are some questions you can ask yourself after being with people you think help your spirit's health. The saying "Raising your spirits" has truth in it. Whatever does that for you is helping your spirit heal and recharge your spiritual body, which helps your energy field be clearer and more vibrant with life force energy.

What is the purpose of spiritual body for our whole body health?

Spirit allows us to see the bigger picture --- long term, not just our immediate human needs or desires. It reminds you that everything is just a moment and moments combine to make up the big picture. It's like missing the forest for the trees. A tree could be seen as a moment a human is in, focused on themselves then and there. The spirit side reminds us to step back and see the forest, all the moments coming together as one overarching journey connecting all the individual trees together to make the forest. Seeing how beautiful it all is --- the broken and burned trees with the vibrant ones are beautiful when they come together. They bring more depth and contrast to look at, the forest has more character and strength in its history. Look what it has survived!

When you're connected to a spirit point of view, you switch perspective to one of gratitude for lessons being learned, reminding you that pain, emotions, and hardships are temporary and will pass. It gives us more hope to get up the next day and love ourselves through all the experiences we have.

Tools to Connect to Spirit and Enhance Our Life force:

- Grounding activities.

- Reading spiritual books.

- Meditation: guided visualizations to quiet mind chatter so you are available to hear your spirit. Being in stillness.

- Breathing exercises.

- Prayer.

- Watching inspirational movies and listening to spiritual music.

- Singing in church or temple - experience connected consciousness by joining the same frequency through song.

Singing helps bring us to "one body" vibrationally - one frequency with God. It strengthens the spirit and clears out lower frequencies.

- The Hu chant is the frequency of God to help connect you to spirit/higher self, clear negative energy from your space.

- A singing bowl can clear the lower frequencies that are stuck in your energy field and replace them with the higher resonance of the heart frequency.

- Baptism --- water, clearing out sin, shame, and negative frequencies from our bodies and spirit. Sins are a lower frequency in us. Rebirth, a fresh start, and forgiveness. All these gifts from baptism help you heal.

Practicing Forgiveness: Finding Peace and Healing on a Spiritual Level

If you are stuck or upset about something in your past --- a relationship or something that happened --- try running these words in a meditation and visualize saying it to the person you are either hurt from, or you feel you hurt, and see if it helps you find forgiveness for them and for yourself in a new way. See if you find your spirit being raised as you forgive and let go of the guilt, shame, or hurt you no longer need to carry in your body or energy field. This helps you bring your frequency up for healing.

Here are some simple phrases to practice from a traditional Hawaiian prayer for forgiveness. It is called Ho'oponopono for forgiveness and to let go of the past on a soul level. The Four Phrases that Can Heal the Spirit:

1. I'm sorry.

2. Please forgive me.

3. Thank you.

4. I love you.

Ho'Oponopono Prayer and Meditation-Directions

1. Close your eyes and get comfortable on a chair, the floor, or laying down.

2. Take a few deep breaths in and out.

3. Now picture either yourself or a person that created pain in your life. Really imagine seeing them. Feel the pain as if that image were real.

4. Now say: **I'm sorry.**

   Please forgive me.

   Thank you.

   I love you.

5. Say each one of these phrases with absolute conviction, feeling true apology, pure forgiveness, pure gratitude and real love. It will take repeating it multiple times. Say it like a mantra again and again.

6. When you sense the person you are imagining is ready to accept the Ho'oponopono, imagine them embracing you with a wave of angelic light and love that eventually merges you both into one. This can be very powerful for your soul and the other person's soul and will help you heal on all levels filling your heart with forgiveness and love frequencies that will put you in a healing state.

This meditation activity is based on the theory that we are all energy, and in that we are all connected. That is why this is one of the highest forms of self-love. You are reclaiming your energy through love and forgiveness. You are also giving others back their energy when you forgive and let go. What a gift this is! It is believed that when you connect in this realm on a spirit level you are connecting with a piece of the universal consciousness, God, or source. This means that you are truly saying these phrases to your own soul and to the person you imagined - your higher self, spirit self, is directly talking to their spirit. You can do a lot of healing work with others in your life just by practicing this mantra from your home. Why not?!

The last thing I am going to share around spiritual body health is the power of asking for help and the use of prayer. Adding in prayer can start to take you to the next level of healing. When we pray and ask for help in our lives, we are surrendering our control and opening up to receive help from a higher power like God or the universe. In asking for support and help we are allowing space inside us to receive in ways we normally might not notice or feel. When we are busy trying to be in control of our life all the time we can miss the opportunities to be vulnerable and accept help when we really need it.

We are all energy and everything is connected, so in prayer you are inviting in outside energy to come and help and heal you or others. It can be very powerful and can be felt by the person asking for the prayers and the person praying. You both end up raising your frequencies to one of love and this in turn helps heal. No prayer is *too* much to ask for. The power of prayer teaches us that the power of intention can heal us by focusing on what you want, not what you don't want. Intention and prayer are very similar and relate to how our thoughts and beliefs can change matter, which is what our physical body is made of.

"For there is always light,
if only we are brave
enough to see it,
if only we are brave
enough to be it."

- Amanda Gorman

PART II
THE CENTER OF THE DIAMOND

The Energy Body

23

The Center of the Diamond: The Energy Body

The center of the diamond is the energy body, which is directly affected by all sides of the diamond. The energy body consists of your life force energy, your auric field, and is also known as the etheric body, prana, and overlaps with spirit in some cultures. The reason the energy body is at the center is that it has been found that if you can identify the imbalanced frequencies in the energy body or in the auric field before they have manifested in the physical body as disease, you can more easily shift them back into a healing state and never have the disease manifest fully in the first place in the physical body. It is much easier to heal if you can identify and work with rebalancing the energy body before it fully becomes a problem in the physical body. And if it has already shown up fully in the physical body, identifying the imbalances in the energy body can greatly increase your ability to heal more quickly and more fully. What I love is when you start making lifestyle changes across the sides of the diamond you are increasing the rebalancing of your energy body. This means it is helping your physical body heal in ways that if you were only focused on treating the physical body through medicine you might not get the results you can when addressing all sides of what makes your *whole* body up. Here is a great explanation from an excerpt from the book *Your Body Doesn't Lie,*

"I have come to believe that all illness starts as a problem that may exist for many years before it manifests itself in physical disease. It appears that a generalized reduction of body energy leads to energy imbalances in particular parts of the body. If we become aware of these energy imbalances when they first occur, we have a long grace period in which to correct them. We will then be practicing primary prevention."

(Pg. 27. Your Body Doesn't Lie)

Life Force Energy

The energy body contains your life force energy. Life force energy is your personal soul's healthy natural energy force that you were born with. It is what gives you vitality and wellness when you are in balance energetically and physically. If it is out of balance, you will have lower energy levels and may feel off or spaced out, heavy, or lost. If your life force is low you are more vulnerable to physical health illnesses and problems frequency-wise.

It is best to be running our own life force energy and not someone else's because we each have a unique fingerprint frequency that is optimal to run on. When we are sick our auric field can become weaker which is one reason you tend to feel more sensitive and want to go into hiding when you are sick. Sometimes when we are so sick that our life force energy is depleted then we need to borrow some life force energy from someone we are very close to, almost like an IV drip, to get us through the crisis. This is something that some people call cording to another person.

Cords connect from one person's energy body, usually through a chakra, to another person's energy body. They allow the exchange of energy between the two people. When you are very sick you are more likely to unconsciously cord to the person who is closest to you, like a parent, family member, or your partner. It is best for both people to only do this for short periods of time until you are able to recharge your energy on your own.

This is another reason it is important to address all sides of the diamond because if you can take responsibility for the things you can do to make each side stronger, you can remove your cord and heal faster using your very own energy. You can also clean up any cords coming into your space or chakras without being aware of it and leaking your energy out. This is what re-writing contracts is helping stop. If you identify where in your relationships you are energetically not balanced and rebalance those relationship by setting boundaries or negotiating new terms that are more balanced then you are actually shifting the energy field and removing cords in your energy field that may be drains in your field. This is one example of how the social, mental, and emotional sides of the diamond end up shifting your energy body.

Auric Field

We all have an auric field (aka an energetic field or the etheric body). This auric boundary around the auric field looks like a bubble around us about two feet off our body all the way around us that acts as a container for the life force inside our bodies and energy field. The auric field has two functions. It protects us from outside energies coming too close and getting inside our bodies. The second is protecting us from other people's energies, which may be vibrating at a different frequency than ours to be healthy.

The auric field acts as a barrier to stop cords from others from coming into your field, a filter to stop all the other needs and manipulations of others around you in your daily life from coming in without realizing it. It helps keep you clean in your space and know that you are separate from others around you. If you are someone who finds that when you are out around others you tend to merge or lose yourself or feel drained or lost, then it may be a sign that your auric field boundary needs strengthening. When the auric field is weak or less defined, it can lead to other people's auric fields coming into yours when you are around them. This can overwhelm people and "spin" them out. It can lead to social anxiety or extreme empaths where they end up feeling everything around them to the point that it is hard to be around a lot of people. Defining your auric field gives you your power back to discern what is yours verses what is other people near you. It doesn't mean you lose your empathy, instead it means you can be more present without becoming drained, overwhelmed, tired, and sick after being around people. So it actually increases your ability to help others by tuning down having to feel everything of theirs in your body and space.

The auric field protects us from negative thoughts, intentions, and unwanted "vibes" from people or the culture around us from coming right in and changing our body's energy and physical body.

The auric field tucks into the grounding cord that connects our body to the earth's core. You might wonder why being grounded is so important to our physical health?

Anatomy of Our Spirit-Physical Body-Energy Body Connection

As I just explained, the auric field is the bubble shaped container that holds in our life force energy and protects our physical body and spirit inside of it.

We live in our physical body. The spirit is inside the physical body. The spirit comes down through the crown chakra at the top of the head into the body. The chakra system runs from the base of our spine up to the top of our skull along the spine (see diagram on next page).

The spirit comes down through the 7th chakra and anchors and connects to the physical body when it comes through the heart chakra (the 4th chakra) and down into the three lower chakras: 1st, 2nd, and 3rd chakras.

The physical body is grounded with a grounding cord to the center of the earth to help discharge energies we run during the day that are no longer needed or helping. The grounding allows the spirit to take hold and root into the physical body better integrating the spirit with the body to be whole and balanced here as a human on Earth.

If your grounding is not clear or connected for some reason then it is harder to stay grounded—you may feel floaty, lightheaded, disconnected from reality. If you have a trauma or crisis happen in your life it can act as an eject button for your spirit to limit the pain, emotional or physical, to your body. You dissociate, which is when the spirit disconnects form the grounding and jumps out of the body temporarily. Sometimes people just have really open 7th chakras that need to be adjusted to a smaller aperture opening so they can stay inside their bodies better.

It is important to know that when you are sick or going through medical things that can cause a lot of discomfort or pain then you are more likely to leave your body some as a way to get through it. The key is to help your body re-ground and clear its energy field once that trauma or event is over enough that it is safe to return fully and feel inside your body again. You can learn to ground yourself and clear your chakras through meditations and prayer to help yourself heal faster and easier.

See the diagram below to better understand the anatomy of the Spirit-Physical Body and Energy Body Connections.

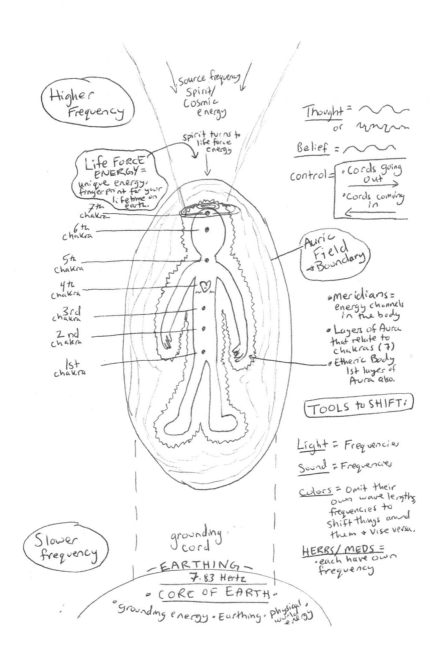

Why is the Energy Body the Center of the Diamond?

Each Side Affects Your Energy Body

Physical Body Side: The physical body is made of energy at its core so adding medicine and supplements, which each have their own frequencies, changes the physical body helping it fight off infections and rebalance chemically. It also helps shift your energy and body into a better frequency of healing if they work correctly.

Another example is the use of grounding and earthing to help physical body healing. Laying on the earth, putting your skin directly on dirt, grass, or water helps your energy field shift into that of the earth which is the same frequency as a healing state. This is a great way to discharge chaotic energies in your field that are affecting your whole body and to sort of hit a reset button by physically touching the earth and being in the magnetic field of it. If you can stay in contact with the earth for at least 30 minutes a day it can really help your healing and symptoms over time.

Mind Body Side: Words and thoughts have their own frequencies, which shift our energy body. Beliefs and intentions have been shown to directly affect and change matter so our thoughts, emotions, and beliefs are powerful and shift our energy body with their distinct frequencies, which in turn manifests in the physical matter that makes our bodies.

Emotional Body Side: All emotions have their own frequencies, which directly shift the energy body, and these frequencies also trigger the production and release of different chemicals in our physical body, which in turn directly affect your physical body systems and structure.

Social Body Side: The people and groups you associate yourself with carry their own frequencies which affect your energy field when you are around them. The bigger and more intensely focused the group is, the stronger their resonance will be and more likely to change your natural life force if you are not in harmony with them or if your auric field is weakened.

Spirit Body Side: Purpose and living in alignment with your spirit or core self-increases your life force which is your God given frequency. Tools like chanting Hu or forgiveness, healing through singing bowls, and meditation can all help us connect with our soul easier and more quickly by shifting our frequency to match that of love, God, light, and the higher powers that be.

Tools to help the Energy Body Rebalance:

- Energy Clearings of the chakras, auric field, energy field and hands on energy healing. Take a shower and bath to wash off and clear energy. You can also sage yourself with a sage mist or smoke.

- Reiki – Find a reiki practitioner near you and see if it helps.

- Watching a sunset or sunrise.

- Being in nature.

- Earthing and grounding: get your bare feet on the earth, grass, dirt outside. Lay on a blanket on the ground for 10-30 minutes. Go swim in a body of water. Take a walk on the beach or near a lake or in a forest.

- Exercising can help release stored or stuck energy like anxiety, anger, rage, shock etc.

- Dancing or Playing.

- Creativity: Journaling, writing, collaging, decorating, painting, doing art, etc.

- Sound Therapy: using singing bowls, bells, and music to clear energy and reset.

- Color Therapy: put colors around you that help you feel calmer, happier, and more at peace. Paint rooms, change your clothes, change the blankets on your bed, use lights with different colors, etc.

- Bioenergetic testing or Muscle Testing: to assess where you may be needing more support physically, herbal and supplement-wise, emotionally, and spiritually.

PART III

Identifying Limiting Factors
in Healing Lyme Disease
and How to Take Action to Support
Your Healing Now

There's a Hole in My Sidewalk

–Portia Nelson, There's a Hole in My Sidewalk:
The Romance of Self-Discovery

"I walk down the street.
There is a deep hole in the sidewalk.
I fall in.
I am lost... I am helpless.
It isn't my fault.
It takes forever to find a way out.

I walk down the same street.
There is a deep hole in the sidewalk.
I pretend I don't see it.
I fall in again.
I can't believe I am in the same place.
But, it isn't my fault.
It still takes me a long time to get out.

I walk down the same street.
There is a deep hole in the sidewalk.
I see it is there.
I still fall in. It's a habit.
My eyes are open.
I know where I am.
It is my fault. I get out immediately.
walk down the same street.
There is a deep hole in the sidewalk.
I walk around it.

I walk down another street."

24

Introduction Part III: Limiting Factors in Healing Lyme Disease

The concept of a limiting factor comes from Chemistry class. I loved it when I learned about it in the 10th grade. When you have a chemical equation, and you are trying to make something, there can be "limiting factors" that prevent you from making your desired outcome. If you don't have enough of a substance you can continue to add all sorts of other elements but without the one you are short on, it won't ever create the outcome you wanted in the first place. This is a limiting factor. There are a few factors when it comes to treating Lyme that can act like this—I will call them "blocks" to treatment and healing.

An example of one of the limiting factors is detoxification. You can add as many meds and supplements as you want but if your body is unable to keep up it will limit your desired outcome of healing Lyme or your chronic illness. The great news is that you can do things to support your body without buying anything expensive or outside of your house even!

This will be a quick summary on this concept since my next book will be going in more detail about physically treating Lyme. I am co-writing it with Naturopath Treya Palmer. She taught me how to identify blocks that I had, and later while working with her, how to identify the blocks our clients had when treating Lyme. She helped me become unlimited by these factors so I could heal form Lyme, to light!

So, let's first look at the limiting factors, or blocks, that affect Lyme treatment and healing, and then I will share some of the things you can do to support your healing.

Inflammation Is at the core of most Limiting Factors and Blocks

Inflammation can be one of the biggest culprits in causing blocks to treatment and healing. If we know there is a big issue blocking our ability to heal then we need to also search for the things that caused it in the first place, or inflammatory triggers. These triggers tend to be the blocks we will be identifying and we will take a quick look at each so you can be aware of where you might need to address triggers in your own body and healing.

When you have inflammation in your body it acts as a block to your treatment. How does it act as a block? One way is that when you are inflamed your body can also become sensitized to whatever meds or supplements you are on to treat your infections. Sensitized means that the med is no longer working well in your body or that your body is not responding as sensitively as it would if you were less inflamed. Over time it takes more of that medication to perform the treatment or a different med all together. This is only one of many ways inflammation causes blocks in your healing. Instead of talking only about inflammation I will go on to share the triggers of inflammation and how these can act as blocks in your Lyme treatment.

One of the goals in your Lyme healing is reducing inflammation in any way you can in your daily life. Here is a list of things that lead to inflammation and can be considered limiting factors or blocks in healing Lyme:

1. High Toxic Burden: Toxicity and the ability to detoxify.

    - Biotoxins, Mycotoxins, Endotoxins, Neurotoxins.

2. Infections: acute and chronic.

3. Environmental exposures - mold, EMF radiation, chemicals, pesticides, perfumes, etc.

4. Inflammatory foods: gluten, dairy, your personal food allergies, sugar, GMOs.

5. Acute and chronic stress: Mental, emotional, or physical

As I go through this section, I want to focus on helping you be able to identify where you might have blocks in your treatment. Once you can identify where these blocks may be occurring you have a better chance of clearing them so your treatments work better.

I hope this will help you come up with questions for your healing team when you feel stuck and help you make decisions that are in your best interest. We can only be responsible by coming out of ignorance and becoming educated instead. This way you can make educated decisions and have more understanding of what is going on inside your body especially when you can feel so overwhelmed like so many of us have with Lyme Disease.

25

Limiting Factors and Block #1: Indentifying Toxicity and Your Ability to Detoxify

One of the main concepts and limiting factors in treating Lyme is toxicity and how well the body is able to detoxify itself.

Oxygen

We live in a pretty toxic world, and it's only getting worse right now. Overall oxygen levels are down from pollution in the air and bodies of water around the world. Fires, smog, and other chemicals we put into our air are adding to this. The decrease in seaweed and overfishing taking place is too fast for nature to rebalance itself and it has been one of the biggest reasons our oxygen levels are down. Why are these oxygen level changes so crucial to you dealing with something like Lyme?

Oxygen is one of nature's most amazing defenses for us humans—it is corrosive to most things while instead, as humans, we can't live without it! On its own oxygen kills most bacteria, viruses, fungi and parasites. That's pretty amazing! If your body is carrying 100 percent of the oxygen that it should it greatly increases your immune system and keeps things in check. Now imagine your clean oxygen supply is decreased percentage-wise and in competition with other toxins in your environment. Can you see how this would directly influence your body's ability to fight off infections?

We rely on oxygen to do some of the natural killing. This is why oxygen therapies as alternative treatments can be helpful for some people who have chronic illnesses like Lyme disease. Hyperbaric chambers and ozone therapies are some examples of these treatments.

Water Bodies

As I am sure you are aware of already, the water on Earth is polluted and now our rain is even dangerous and toxic. Lakes are so polluted and out of balance throughout the world you can't swim in them anymore due to algae and bacteria from run off waste, pesticides, and chemicals. These critters and toxins get into our bodies through exposures from drinking or wading adding to our toxic load we need to clean out of our bodies.

Buildings and Indoor Environments

Our homes and buildings are built out of dry wall which is essentially a form of paper and conductive to mold growth with small amounts of moisture. Molds produce mycotoxins that are harmful to our health and cause inflammation in our bodies. Our houses are built using woods full of formaldehyde and other chemicals that off gas. Our bodies are bombarded by toxins everywhere we go at this point. This is why more and more people are becoming sick with chronic illnesses like Lyme disease, Chronic Fatigue Syndrome, Lupus, MS, long hall COVID, etc.

I am just trying to paint a picture of what type of environment we all live in as beings on Earth currently before going into our individual home environments and bodies. The good news is we have some say in what we expose ourselves to on a daily basis especially when we become aware of these challenges.

Internal Body Toxins

On top of the toxic world we live in we are also exposed to infections and bacteria inside our internal environments - our bodies. These critters create toxins in our bodies as well. You heard me right. Did you know that Lyme itself creates byproducts or biotoxins inside you? And as you kill the Lyme you release more of these toxins before fully cleaning the dead Lyme bodies out. Co-infections and fungi all create biotoxins inside us in the form of neurotoxins, endotoxins, and biotoxins. Each of these toxins also comes with their own set of symptoms and challenges when inside of us. All these byproducts start adding to your toxic load, which I like to call the *toxic burden*.

Toxic Burden

The Toxic Burden is like a bucket; sometimes our bodies are healthy and keep the toxins in check, emptying the bucket before it becomes full. But then you get exposed to an infection like Lyme Disease or COVID-19 and your immune system is overloaded with the new threat and your already moderate toxic burden, from living in our toxic world, increases. Now your toxic burden, your bucket, is full and maybe even overflowing so you get sick. The more toxic you are the sicker you will feel because the inflammation level in your entire body goes up!

The concept I like to use to explain this is the fish tank theory. You have a fish in a fishbowl that is clean. It's healthy and happy. Then the bowl gets dirty, and the fish gets symptoms of being sick. The fish doctor wants to prescribe meds for the fish's symptoms but ignores the fact the water that the fish is living in, the environment it is in, is dirty. Instead of cleaning the tank first, the true cause of the symptoms, the doctor prescribes meds for the presenting symptoms. Adding meds means adding more chemicals and byproducts to the fish and to the tank because the fish poops it into the water. The toxic burden increases. The fish may feel a little relief while on the meds, which are reducing the bacteria inside it, but once done the fish falls sick again and feels worse since the water is even dirtier.

So, the fish decides to go to see an integrative or functional doctor and they say to the fish "well we have to clean the bowl before we treat the symptoms. The fishbowl needs to be rebalanced and clean to get the cause of your illness in check."

Treat the cause at the base. The fish gets better when the water is clean. The meds can work to rid the infections it had since its body could keep up with detoxification, rebuild immunity, and decrease inflammation. The fish's toxic burden goes down and the symptoms go away.

Remember the body is constantly trying to stay in a state of homeostasis. Adjusting its biochemistry, balancing pH in the blood, hydration, elimination, and filtering out good guys verses the bad guys in your system.

It's complex but at the same time the concept is simple—your body wants to remain in a state of balance, and for it to do this the systems need to stay clear and healthy. If one system gets backed up then other systems don't work right and get overburdened.

Let's say the liver is overburdened with toxins that start to spill over into the blood. Now the spleen and lymphatic system start getting overworked and you get lymphatic backup—swollen glands and bloating can be signs of this. Then what happens is you get toxic overall and your brain's chemistry becomes imbalanced. Serotonin levels go down and you may become depressed or less motivated to exercise or eat right. You start to crave carbs to give you a quick serotonin and oxytocin hit. The carbs feed the bad bacteria and infections, so now you are adding more toxins with the junk food your brain is craving. This becomes a toxic slump that can be overwhelming to get yourself out of. If you start at the base by making sure you are supporting your detoxification by cleaning house and getting the right nutrition or supplements, then symptoms tend to go down and healing can happen a lot faster.

> ### It's this simple: One of the main limiting factors in treating Lyme Disease or any chronic illness tends to be how well and how fast your body can detoxify.

If you are toxic the systems in your body become deregulated and start to malfunction or shut down. Medications and supplements you take to treat the infections don't work as well since the systems (i.e., immune, lymphatic, digestive, methylation, hormonal, and neurological) are in disharmony from the toxic overload.

The great news is there are a lot of basic things you can do to help your body clean house! And that is what I am going to share in the coming pages as well as in the next book coming out. This is where you can make changes in your lifestyle and thinking that can help you get better quicker and feel better while you are in treatment.

But before you start doing anything to support your healing, it is super important to remember to take it slowly! You do not want to start treating too much too fast. It can and will overload your body's ability to keep up as you clean house. You need to start off slow and gentle when it comes to adding new supplements or activities to help you detox. It can be dangerous to "push" your detoxification too fast because you can become too toxic too quickly! So when you are in treatment and getting meds always remember that if you start having signs of your toxic burden increasing then it is a clue to slow down and call your health practitioner. It's like you turned a key and opened the door and it all wants to flood out; you have to slowly open that door and control the flow so you don't get blown down by what's behind it.

Here is a short list of some of the signs that your toxic burden may be going up:

- Difficulty concentrating or brain fog

- Nasal/sinus congestion

- Skin symptoms (acne, breakouts, eczema, redness)

- Digestive problems (diarrhea, indigestion, acid reflux, etc.)

- Fatigue or achy joints

- Brittle toenails

- Hair loss

- Bloating

- Bad breath

- Nausea

- Headaches

- Irritability

- Sugar cravings

- Trouble losing weight

Some things you can do daily at home to support your detoxification system:

WATER: Drink lots of clean filtered water.

BINDERS: Take a low dose binder to help take toxins out (talk to your doctor about adding one - NDs are very helpful with this). An example of a gentle binder is cilantro, which is a natural binder for heavy metals that you can use in your meals.

- Remember you want to always start slowly and work up on doses of supplements or meds that support detoxification, always under the care of a medical professional.

SAUNA: If you do choose to use a sauna please go slow. They push your detoxification processes which is good but you want to detoxify slowly so you don't overdo it in one day. Start out once to twice a week at a low time limit like 15 minutes. Then gradually increase the time to 20 minutes and see how you are feeling. If you feel better after the saunas then you did the right amount of time. If you feel worse then take it down a notch. Everyone is different so there is no size that fits all. It is just one of many tools you can have to help yourself detoxify. Be sure to drink water and add electrolytes if you sweat a lot. You can do this through a packet of electrolyte mix that you add to water or through the food you eat. Talk to your doctor if you have questions or want to check if it is right for you. The sauna not only works on the detoxification in your body but the heat also helps your immune system kill infections. This is another reason you do not want to do too much at once especially in the beginning. Start slow and short times. Increase gradually. Going fast doesn't mean you will get better faster. It actually ends up taking longer and is way more painful when you push your body with Lyme. So slow and gentle wins the race.

ENEMAS: Enemas can be done in the comfort of your own home bathroom. You can buy a kit at a drugstore and all you will need is clean filtered water, your kit, and some lube or oil and you are ready to go. Release 1-3 bags over a half hour total. Enemas can also be done with coffee to increase glutathione in your body to support the liver. Either way can help you bring down a high toxic burden quicker. People who are experiencing symptoms of a high toxic burden find that after one enema session a lot of those symptoms subside. At the very least their brains feel clearer and they start to feel better. There are lots of ways to do an enema. I would recommend talking to your health practitioner or integrative doctor who is familiar with them. You may also go to a Colon Hydro-therapist for a colonic to learn more and get a treatment. Colonics are a great way to do the same thing and they go much deeper than an enema does. I go much more into this as a tool in the next book, but for now I wanted you to know this can be a great tool to healing. Plus, its affordable, safe, and easy to do!

LYMPHATIC SUPPORT: The lymphatic system is super important in our bodies ability to detoxify properly. The lymphatic system is a passive system, meaning it needs active movement or pressures from outside itself to pump and work properly. This means we have to move our bodies and gently do things to have it work. Deep breathing is one way we move our lymphatic system daily, but walking, moving, bouncing, and swimming all help move it. The lymph system's main function is to remove toxins from our blood. The lymph nodes are centers in the system that filter these toxins out like bacteria, viruses, fungi, cancer cells, etc. It also helps balance the fluids in our body. If the lymph system becomes backed up you may experience bloating, water retention, and swelling of lymph nodes. The good news is there are things you can do at home for free or cheap to help support your lymphatic system in staying healthy. Here is a list of ideas to add to your daily program:

Walking

Swimming or bouncing in the water

Taking a bath with Epsom salts

Rebounding on a small trampoline

Bouncing gently while seated on the side on your bed

Massage: A Lymphatic Massage or Gentle Swedish Massage (not deep tissue- this will release a ton of toxins and may overwhelm your system).

Deep breathing exercises

Gentle stretching or Gentle Yoga

Key Terms to Know:

Biotoxins: They are poisonous substances produced by a living organism. Let's take a look at a few types that we see in Lyme infected people:

- **Mycotoxins:** They are toxins produced by fungi or molds that are known to create disease and even cause death in humans and other animals. They can be inhaled, ingested, or taken in topically making their host sick with a variety of symptoms. They tend to create inflammation and wreak havoc on many of the body's systems. Living or working in moldy buildings can cause these to build up in your body. You may also ingest mycotons from either meat that was fed moldy grain or mold in your actual foods. Some examples of mycotoxins causing human and animal illness are aflatoxin, citrinin, fumonisins, ochratoxin A, and trichothecenes. This is why getting ERMI testing of your home or work can be very helpful if you suspect you have mycotoxin exposures contributing to your health issues.

- **Endotoxins:** They are toxins that are present inside a bacterial cell. They are released as endotoxins into the body when a cell breaks down causing the host to feel ill from the toxins being released. The immune system reacts to these toxins as foreign invaders when they are released so you end up with symptoms of immune response like achy body, inflammation, fever, chills, etc. These symptoms can be characteristic of a disease. When you hear someone talk about "die off" reactions a lot of them are caused by these toxins being released as you kill off an infection. Sometimes you feel worse before you are better.

- **Neurotoxins:** These are toxins or poisons that act on your nervous system when exposed to them. You tend to have symptoms like headaches, brain fog, migraines, tics, numbness and tingling, neurological issues, etc. Neurotoxins can be ingested, inhaled, or taken in through the skin. Some infections put off neurotoxins as they die and the cell breaks down. Fun fact: Did you know skunk spray is a neurotoxin? That's why you can get headaches from it or feel dizzy when exposed to it. Special thanks to my labradoodle Lilli for teaching me that after getting skunked in the face twice.

Detoxification: The process of removing toxic substances or qualities from your body or life.

Toxic Burden: The total amount of toxins you have on board in your body at a given time. These toxins include, but are not limited to, biotoxins, chemicals, heavy metals, etc.

What happens when your body's toxic burden increases?

Toxins can damage the enzymes in your body. Enzymes are crucial to almost every function and chemical reaction in your body's systems to be alive and balanced. One example is toxins can damage the production of hemoglobin, altering your blood's ability to carry oxygen and iron. This can accelerate aging. It also leads to mitochondria, the powerhouse of the cells, breaking down and not working right so you will have less energy and protection against oxidative stress. Enzymes are crucial in hormonal balance and production of immune responses. Failure of these normal body processes greatly increases your risk of diseases like Lyme and can act as a block in your healing if not corrected or supported.

Summary

If you don't support your detoxification system when the toxic burden is high then you will have no room to add more treatments or kill infections without creating more stress in your body. You will feel sicker, and your treatments will not work as well as they should. You need to support detoxification and monitor how toxic you are throughout your treatments so you can get the help in adjusting the dose and going slower when you need to. This will increase your recovery and treatment time. You also will gain quality in your daily life when you have fewer symptoms that usually correlate with higher toxic burden levels in your body.

26

Limiting Factor #2:
Identifying and Prioritizing Infection

The main concept here is that infections, whether bacterial, viral, parasitic, fungal, etc, all have different priorities and energy. It can be crucial to address some infections before others if you want to make better progress in treatment. Before I knew about this concept I struggled by trying to treat Lyme on its own first. The problem was I had co-infections and parasites that were blocking my body's ability to treat the Lyme because the parasites were a higher priority to my immune system. It was showing up as the immediate threat. Meanwhile I was focused on treating the Lyme but not getting anywhere because my body didn't want meds for Lyme, it wanted help with the parasites first. That being said I could gently treat the Lyme in the background while I switched my focus to going after the parasites that were blocking me. My immune system knew what threat needed to go first and once I learned more about why certain infections tend to be priorities it greatly increased my success in treating the Lyme and all infections I was dealing with. It also helped me to decrease how many meds I needed for much shorter periods of time. Please know that a lot of doctors aren't even aware of this and that is okay. This is another reason why it is important to find a health practitioner that is well versed in Lyme and the multiple co-infections it presents with, and having some sort of integrative medicine background or training can really help. I want you to understand this as a concept in case you keep finding you aren't making progress with one of the infections you are trying to treat. You might stop and ask yourself - what could be blocking me? Could it be another infection that my immune system wants to go after first? Since you are most likely not a doctor, you can seek out what other infections you may be carrying with your physician. Using muscle testing or bioenergetic testing to help prioritize the order in which you treat can be very helpful as well.

On the next page are some examples of how different infections might be prioritized in your treatment (it is slightly different for each person, this is only an example.)

Priority of Treatment - What to focus on to remove blocks and heal faster from Lyme:

1. High Toxic Burden - Gently support detoxification first. Using low dose binders, supplements and activities to help your detoxification system rebalance.

   - CIRS and Mold Illness can be blockers due to the high level of inflammation they cause in the body and gut. You need to support your immune system with binders. Seek treatment with a trained mold illness professional if you suspect you are experiencing mold illness with Lyme disease.

   Parasites - H. pylori and other bacterial gut infections can block your body's ability to absorb the meds you take to treat other things. Getting those down and under control can increase your efficiency in treating other infections like Lyme. Lyme also takes residence in the gut so it's like peeling off the layers to get to it. Please note heavy metals can be an issue when eradicating the parasites so binders may be needed to support detox.

2. C. Pneumonia can be a block as well and it can be in gut lining.

3. Lyme and Co-Infections.

4. Other Bacterial infection like strep strains, etc. This may come before Lyme depending on each person.

5. Low Grade Chronic Viral Load.

6. Retroviruses.

7. Vaccine injuries.

8. Support and repair mitochondrial function, mineral imbalances, hormones, and gut health (you do some of this in the background throughout your program but near the end you focus on boosting it all and repairing damage from the infections once they are gone to rebuild immunity).

-End of Example-

For now, this is all I am going to share about infections as a block in this book. The next book is where you can learn more about this and other limiting factors introduced in this chapter. I have co-written the next book with a Naturopath who focused on Lyme treatment for over 25 years. It has a lot of amazing information that we hope will help you on your healing journey.

Blood and Urine Tests for Lyme and Co-infections:

You need to see the right health professional to get the best blood tests to figure out what is causing your illnesses. Finding a Lyme literate specialist to order the blood work needed to diagnose and treat Lyme is extremely important in your journey.

IGeneX Lab is great for ruling out and diagnosing Lyme and many of its co-infections. If you have Medicare, you are in luck because the testing is covered in full. If not then you will need to look at the cost and know what you are paying for. The great news is if it is your first Lyme and Co-infection round of testing there is a Lyme Tap Grant available through the Rotary Club that you can apply for depending on your income level at the time. You can get up to 80% of your money back. This helps people get the testing they need in the beginning to know if they have Lyme or not. It's a huge help and worth the investment to get IGeneX testing if you suspect you have Lyme or co-infections. You order a blood test kit for $20 on their website and then take it to your doctor to fill in the request. Then you can get the blood drawn. There are other testing companies starting up as well so always check with your doctor on what they want to use. IGeneX tends to be accurate, which can be hard to find in Lyme testing. DNA Connections is another company you can check into. I have not used their testing but have heard they are good. See below.

Resources:

- IGeneX: https://IGeneX.com

- Lyme Tap Grant for first time testing: https://www.Lymetap.com

- DNA Connections: https://dnaconnexions.com/product/Lyme-panel-order-test/

An Optional Helpful Tool to help Prioritize Treatment:

Bioenergetic Testing

As I introduced in Part I of this book, a helpful tool to figure out your treatment priorities can be through Bioenergetic testing. I truly believe that bioenergetic testing is going to be a key to medicine in the future. It is noninvasive, easy to run and can give a ton of information that, if used in combination with Western Medicine (i.e., blood tests, laboratory testing and patient history gathering), you can really help address all sides of the person's health and body.

Each person's needs can differ when treating the same illness or disease because we all have different environments, genes, stress levels, and make ups. There is no one exactly like you at any given time! You are unique and beautiful and amazing just as you are. You also have your own deficiencies and needs to fully heal so one treatment doesn't always cure all. Luckily, we are all humans so there is enough similarity that we can usually treat illness but to hone in on the specific needs each person's body has while doing these treatments can be a game changer. Bioenergetic testing addresses this factor - that each of our bodies needs something a little different than the next. Adding something like this to general medicine is an amazing tool to help the patient and doctor find success in treatments, which is a win-win for all involved (except maybe pharmaceuticals if it means getting better faster).

Resources to Learn More

Autonomic Response Testing: This is a simple, yet highly effective biofeedback assessment technique used to determine disturbances, imbalances, and possible remedies in your body. It is an advanced form of muscle testing and is noninvasive. Look for a certified practitioner to do the testing.

Find a Health Practitioner trained in Kinesiology (muscle testing). Some chiropractors, Naturopathic doctors, and Osteopathic doctors are trained in this.

Learn about muscle testing yourself through self-testing for smaller things you need to check like what makes your body feels stronger or not.

You can search for bioenergetic testing, muscle testing, or behavioral Kinesiology online to learn more about who may be near you for testing.

27

Limiting Factor #3: Identifying Toxic Environmental Exposures

Outside of the fact of all the things causing the toxic burden in your body to increase that I discussed in prior chapters on detoxification, here are some of the specific things that fall under Environmental Exposures so you can identify them more easily and clear blocks in your healing.

1. Mold Exposure

Mold in your environment can wreak havoc on your health. Molds and fungi produce the biotoxins called mycotoxins which can be very dangerous for your health. Mycotoxins can be inhaled, ingested, or taken in through your skin and cause a range of symptoms, especially triggering chronic inflammatory response in patients with Lyme or other immune compromising conditions. There's also a gene called the HLA gene, which about 25% of the population has, that can be activated when exposed to mycotoxins for longer periods of time. Once the gene is turned on it can make it very hard for your body to detoxify the mycotoxins so you begin to store them in your fat to protect your body from their poisons. Over time your toxic burden becomes very high and you become ill from the exposures. The good news is if you realize you have the HLA gene and that you are getting exposed to mycotoxins you can take special binders and do things to take the toxins out of your body. Seeing a mold specialized doctor is key to getting the right treatment plan started for you. Dr. Shoemaker has a lot of information on this on his website: www.survivingmold.com.

Some Signs and Symptoms of Mycotoxin Exposure or Mold Illness:

1. Chronic inflammation

2. Cognitive difficulties like brain fog, poor memory, poor concentration, anxiety, depression

3. Metallic taste

4. Pain in muscles, joints, or abdomen. Can present as fibromyalgia (especially abdominal pain, but can include muscle pain similar to fibromyalgia)

5. Unexplained weight gain or weight loss

6. Numbness and tingling in extremities or other areas of the body

7. Vertigo or dizziness

8. Hair loss

9. Skin rashes

10. Tinnitus

11. Digestive issues like increase in food sensitivities or reaction, persistent bloating, constipation or diarrhea

12. Serious fatigue that interferes with daily activities

13. Changes in mood stability like anxiety, manic depression or bipolar disorder, ADHD/ADD

14. Excessive thirst and dehydration

15. Hormone imbalances

Mold Testing in Your Environment

The ERMI Test is used for testing your environment for mold. I encourage you to do your own searching and interviewing before deciding where to get your ERMI test, but I will provide two resources for you below. Dr. Shoemaker's website also has information about it. I am not recommending either/or, just giving you resources to get you started.

- Envirobiomics: https://www.envirobiomics.com/

- MycoMetrics: https://www.mycometrics.com/ermi.html

- Blood work and Urine Testing list for helping diagnose mold illness and CIRS:

   - I will refer you to Dr. Shoemaker's website which can be very helpful in finding all the info you need about mold illness, diagnosis, and treatment. You can share it with your doctor or better yet find a Surviving Mold Certified doctor to work with you. Website: https://www.survivingmold.com/

Some examples of labs that offer tests for mycotoxins are: RealTime Labs, Great Plains Labs, My Myco Lab, and Cyrex Labs. Ask them to run Array 12 which looks at the immune reaction to many pathogens including molds, or order an **Organic Acids Test** to see potential yeast or mold colonization as well as give information on how to best support your body systems. Check with your doctor on what is best for you.

Online or in Person Eye Test to Screen for Mycotoxin Exposures:

- Optional Self Screening: VCS (Visual Contrast Sensitivity) testing

   - This test is designed off the findings that the optic nerve is affected by biotoxins, which is measurable by evaluating the eye's ability to discern contrast. This was developed by the Department of Defense to screen soldiers for potential biotoxin exposure. It is **not** a diagnostic test. If it's positive then it means there is a 90% chance of exposure to a biotoxin, which can be from mycotoxins or endotoxins from other infections. It costs under $20 and it can be done at home online anytime.

2. Identifying Chemicals, Pesticides and Heavy Metals

Pesticides, Herbicides, and Fungicides, like glyphosate and other organophosphates, have made their way into our food, our air, and our bodies. They are everywhere in everyone. It is a matter of how much exposure you are getting in your daily life and choosing to limit your exposure when you can.

Formaldehyde: This chemical can be found in most buildings. It is in most new carpets, new clothing, new mattresses, new cars, some foods and cosmetics, and in woods used in construction. It tends to off gas in newer items, dissipating its intensity over time. Using an air purifier can help decrease its toxic effects. It is best to try to limit exposures to it when you can and to become aware of it while healing so you can avoid it when it is a stressor for your body.

Synthetic perfumes which can be found in detergents, cleaning supplies, cosmetics and more are hard for the body to break down since they are foreign to the body's system. They can add to your toxic burden making you more and more chemical sensitive in the long run. It is great if you can go through the daily products you expose yourself to and switch out those things that list "perfume" in the ingredients. Essential oils are natural and the body is able to break them down in small doses, but perfumes are not. Choose essential oils for scents instead of man-made perfumes.

Heavy metals: Mercury, cadmium, lead, and other harmful heavy metals can be found in our soil, water, and food. A major exposure risk is right inside your mouth if you had dental work prior to the discontinuation of metal fillings. These fillings over time can leak heavy metals into your body. It is another source to be aware of.

Polyfluoroalkyl substances (PFAS): This toxin can be found in Teflon and Scotch Guard. They are resistant to breakdown and are found in our soil and groundwater. For years the chemical companies covered up PFAS' health risks, which include inflammation, immune system deregulation, cancer, and other diseases. It is very commonly found in our tap water. It is a good idea to make sure your drinking water is tested, filtered, and clean and you aren't just assuming your tap water is safe to use, especially for internal ingestion. This is for ruling out all toxins, not just this one.

Overall chemicals, perfumes, heavy metals, plastics, and pesticides can all act as blocks in our body due to their high toxicity. They can create blocks in our detoxification systems or deficiencies in enzyme production leading to lowered energy and poorer health.

We all know that these things come with a list of warnings about how they can negatively impact health so I don't need to get further into it. When healing Lyme you want to keep in mind whether you could possibly have any toxic build up in these areas. You can ask yourself the following questions:

- Have you had heavy metal fillings in your teeth?

- Have you had a chemical or pesticide exposure?

- What do you expose yourself to in your daily life that could be building up over time and adding to your toxic burden?

    Perfumes, cleaners, detergents and even products like body lotion or shampoo can carry small amounts of chemicals that can add to our body's stress.

- Are you eating pesticides on food?

- Do you live or work near a farm that sprays pesticides? You may be breathing them in.

- Have you had your tap water or well water tested?

These are factors that you can have some control over by changing your daily habits to choose more green and healthy products to expose yourself to. Remember every bit helps but also don't stress yourself out over the small stuff. Do what you can, when you are ready. One step at a time.

Testing for These Toxins in Your Body

If you want to rule out chemicals and heavy metals as blocks in your treatment there are tests you can do to see if it's affecting you.

There are urine, hair, and blood tests to help you find out if chemicals or heavy metals are playing a negative role in your treatment. There are many companies that offer this testing. It will most likely cost you out of pocket but the information can be very helpful in understanding what treatments your doctor can add to help your body clear out the old junk!

Also please note that if you do have heavy metal toxicity from fillings in your teeth you really want to work with an experienced dentist who also understands Lyme disease. It's very important to not do too much in one visit because your body has to keep up with the detoxification of the metal from taking the fillings out. The dentist also has to keep the metal from going into your body as they remove it. A biological dentist or integrative dentist can be a good place to start.

Ask your health practitioner if he or she does testing for these things if you feel like this is an area that may be blocking your healing. If your general practitioner is not familiar with it then working with a Naturopathic Doctor or integrative doctor may be better.

16. Electromagnetic frequency (EMF) Radiation and Sensitivity

EMF Sensitivity is a newer concept that's becoming better known within medicine as we increase our use of electronics and cell devices around the world. Electromagnetic frequencies from Wi-Fi, cell phones, computers, tablets, and other devices can have a negative impact on physical health by affecting systems regulated by voltage-gated calcium channels. These channels are significant for dozens of essential biological functions and processes. It is not just outside symptoms we feel, but the DNA in our cells recognizes EMF at very low levels. This causes our bodies to produce a biochemical response to these fields, meaning it starts to change our physical body in negative ways just by being exposed. We all know in today's world it is almost impossible to get away from using EMF devices in our daily lives so instead finding ways to limit or counteract these exposures will help you stop yourself from becoming sensitive to them.

If someone is sensitive to EMF Radiation, even at small doses, it can trigger a whole list of symptoms and health issues. Some of them are:

1. headaches

2. dizziness/nausea

3. memory and concentration difficulties

4. insomnia

5. depression/anxiety

6. fatigue/weakness

7. numbness/tingling

8. muscle and joint pains

9. heart palpitations

10. shortness of breath

11. heart arrhythmias

12. high blood pressure

13. Eyes pain/discomfort, pressure in the eyes, deteriorating vision, cataracts

14. Ears may have ringing or hearing loss

15. Skin problems

16. digestive problems

17. dehydration

18. nosebleeds

19. impaired sense of smell

20. light sensitivity

21. Tingling and numbness in hands while holding a device

22. Blood thickening or clumping under microscope when near EMF

Quick Tools or Ideas to Lower EMF in your Life:

Turn off Wi-Fi at night while you sleep: This is huge in helping your brain's lymphatic system, called your glymphatic system, detoxify while you sleep. Many studies have shown that being exposed to Wi-Fi at night can block the detoxification pathways of the brain leading to insomnia, dementia, and concentration issues from toxicity building up in the brain. Most of the detoxification for our brains takes place while we sleep so it is a great time to give our houses and bodies a break from the Wi-Fi exposure.

- OR try using ethernet cablse instead of Wi-Fi on all your devices. This gets rid of all Wi-Fi EMF exposure in your home (remember to disable the Wi-Fi on your router/modem). Bad news is it doesn't block your exposure from your neighbors Wi-Fi, but it does decrease the intensity since it isn't so close to you while you live and sleep.

EMF Blocking Sleep Canopy: You can order an EMF Blocking Sleep Canopy to go over your bed. You'll want to read instructions and make sure you do it correctly. This can be a great way to get a break from EMF exposures while you sleep. Please know that if you choose to get one you might feel worse at first because it will unblock detoxification pathways and your body will start detoxifying faster than it could before. This can lead to symptoms of toxicity at first but soon you will feel better. Add some enemas, saunas, and lymphatic support and you can even gradually expose yourself to the low EMF inside the canopy. Going slow is always better than pushing detoxification too fast. You can find these canopies online.

EMF Lowering Phone Cases: They lower the radiation you receive while talking on or holding your cell phone. Use wired headsets as well to keep EMF radiation away from your brain.

Use a landline: If it is an option. Overall, these are outdated and hard to get set up, but the good news is there is no EMF from corded phones. Cordless phones still have EMF.

EMF Meter Device: You can buy an EMF meter device to check EMF exposure in your living and working environments. They are about $100-$300 for a good one.

28

Limiting Factor #4: Identifying Inflammatory Food Triggers

Choosing foods that are right for you is important. The general concept here is that foods that cause inflammation should be avoided or cut down on to promote your healing and treatment.

Personal Food Allergies

One thing that can be a huge help finding places in your diet that may be causing blocks in your treatment is by getting a food allergy panel done. A food allergy panel will help tell you which foods and or food groups cause your body to become inflamed. If you have leaky gut these allergies go up in importance. The good news is if you heal your leaky gut, at some point in the future you most likely will be able to add back some of the foods you may react to now. The more inflamed you are the more foods you will be reactive to, so getting that inflammation down will most likely mean being able to add back things you enjoy in the future. But for now you have to be strict and avoid the foods you react to so your body has some time to heal.

The best way to get testing done for this is to talk to your health care practitioner. If they don't know about it ask for a referral or find a doctor who does. Most integrative doctors and naturopathic doctors know about food sensitivity testing and food allergy testing. If you are struggling with Lyme and coinfections, it is important to avoid any foods that provide any reaction to stop the cascade of leaky gut and immune reactivity, and reduce your inflammation markers. So, what I am saying is it is good to get tested for food allergy sensitivities if you are asked about both.

I go into detail about leaky gut in relation to Lyme and the cascade of effects it has on your treatment in the next book coming out, but for now this is enough of a summary to get you thinking about food allergies and sensitivities acting as blocks.

Food Allergy Testing

Your doctor's office may have a company they prefer to use, so the first thing to do is talk about getting the testing done with your health professional. I do want to warn you that food allergy testing may have some out-of-pocket cost but it is worth looking into in the long run because food allergies can wreak havoc over time.

Food allergy testing can be done through many modalities: blood work, scratching testing, muscle testing, and through urine samples.

Resource: Cyrex Labs: https://www.cyrexlabs.com/

GMOs

It is well known that Genetically Modified Foods (GMOs) may pose threats around toxicity, allergic reactions, antibiotic resistance, immunosuppressant, cancer, and a lack or loss of nutrition in the plants that are being modified. I first learned about the potential negative health outcomes from a conference I went to on healing the brain from neurological degeneration. The neurologist shared all the research he had done on GMOs, the devastating symptoms he saw in people who were eating them, and what happened when they cut GMOs out of their diet. They got better! A lot better! It may not have cured them because there were many things going on, but it greatly improved their chances of surviving things like cancer, dementia, and many other diseases. They were able to heal from them and make better progress with their meds. Greatest of all, the symptoms that had caused these patients to live with pain and low energy greatly decreased. At the time of the conference I was still trying to heal the lingering issues I had with Chronic Fatigue, especially Brain Fatigue and feeling Lyme symptoms in my body. Even though I was doing so much better than I had when I started treatment, I still wanted to get my life back and feel vitality in what I was doing once again. It had honestly been years since I felt that. I decided to try it with my partner Adam. We switched out all food in our kitchen with groceries that said organic or non-GMO and made a pact to only eat that way for 3 months to see how it changed us. We were still making our same meals just switching out the GMOs for non-GMOs. We were blown away with the differences we felt within two weeks, and we haven't gone back to GMOs since. My brain fatigue got so much better, the inflammation in my body went down, and I got less sick throughout the year. I needed less supplements over time. It was a game changer. We only come off this diet when traveling, because we know it may be hard to find food of this quality while on the road, but we try our best to still limit the GMOs. When we do eat out it's amazing how much worse we both feel. Achy, tired, bloated, flu-ish…

Choosing to eat non-GMO foods can be a game changer for people who have immune system challenges and inflammation. I am encouraging you to find foods that either say "organic" on them, which automatically means they are non-GMO, or if you can't find organic then non-GMO is best. There is research explaining how GMOs can negatively affect the immune system and neurological function. They can trigger autoimmune conditions and lead to cancer. GMOs are something you can choose to cut out of your diet that can have major beneficial outcomes on your healing process. When buying meat look for ones that are organic or fed non-GMO grain; grass fed or pasture raised can help too.

Sugar

Sugar is inflammatory. It's that simple. A spoonful of sugar is all it takes to weaken your thymus gland for hours which acts as a sort of controller for your immune system. The thymus gland tells the body to make white blood cells as a defense against infectious invaders. Take someone with Lyme Disease and its co-infections. One of the main focuses in treatment is waking the immune system back up to do its job since Lyme Spirochetes secrete an enzyme that tells the immune system to go to sleep. These are all very simplified explanations but my goal in this book is to give you the general concept of why things are important to take into account and how it all works as a bigger picture.

The good news is that it is within your control to put sugar into your body or not. It may take some self-discipline and some label reading but it is something you can do to help your body on a daily basis. If you want something sweet organic local honey, organic apples, and organic berries do not lower the thymus gland and are safer to consume. Some people love organic stevia which is also something that can help kill Lyme. Everything in moderation though, right?

Sugar also feeds the bugs! You are giving them exactly what they want to survive and multiply. Sugar feeds co-infections like candida and parasites that lower your gut's microbiome and adds biotoxins to your toxic burden over time.

By cutting out sugar as much as you can you increase the effectiveness of your treatment by essentially starving the infections while hitting them with medications and supplements. Eating a diet with whole organic or non-GMO foods like veggies and meat, and limiting fast carbohydrates that break down into sugar, will help immensely.

Gluten

It will be important to get testing done for celiac disease and gluten intolerance to avoid creating a block for your healing. If you show any sensitivity to gluten it is important for you to avoid it all together while in treatment for Lyme. This will cause your immune system to be chronically inflamed if you continue to be exposed to gluten. If you have celiac disease then you will need to avoid it for the rest of your life. If you only have a sensitivity then you need to avoid it until you are done with treatment and your gut health is balanced. Then you can sometimes try bringing it back in, but you may still react to it. A lot of people choose to not add it back to be safe once they have become used to not having it.

Dairy

It is important to know if you are lactose intolerant because, if you are, ingesting it can cause a cascade of inflammatory responses that will leave you feeling achy, tired, sick, and bloated. Not to worry. If you are lactose intolerant, or you think you might be, you can usually still ingest sheep and goat products instead. At first they taste quite different but over time most people grow to like them. One of the best things you can do is alternate between the two and only eat or drink it in moderation so you do not become sensitized to it as well. I love being able to get hard sheep's cheese and grate it on a cauliflower crust pizza to get my pizza fix without all the stuff I can't eat. Better yet, I don't feel sluggish, tired, or bloated after consuming it!

There are so many alternatives to dairy as well like oat milk, coconut milk, almond milk, soy milk, and rice milk. I love making a low sugar hot chocolate with organic oat milk and a square of organic non-dairy dark chocolate! Its better than any of the hot chocolate full of dairy and sugar I used to love to drink. It's all about finding new combos to bring joy to eating!

Remember to Bring Joy to Your Meals!

Sometimes when we change our diets to be healthier we feel like we are eliminating all the joy of eating, but it doesn't have to be that way. There are so many more options that are organic, non-GMO, gluten free, dairy free, plant-based, whole ingredient foods so you can make almost anything you used to love. It just takes a little extra time at first to learn and to make a habit out of it. Have fun exploring and learning!

29

Limiting Factor #5:
Identifying Acute and Chronic Stress

As we all know stress can cause a ton of negative effects on our health and healing. Both acute and chronic stress can be blocks in healing Lyme if they are not identified, addressed, or supported in some way with things like rest, boundaries, supplements, or other lifestyle changes.

Acute stress is any immediate stress that the body is dealing with for a shorter period of time like when you catch a cold, are outside in the snow without enough clothing, or you experience a small crisis. When you are in this heightened stress period your body releases a cascade of fight or flight hormones as though your life is being threatened in some way. These chemicals can act as temporary blocks in your treatment or lower your body's ability to heal.

Chronic stress is when your body is being stressed continuously over an extended period of months or years. These stresses can come as physical, mental, emotional, or a combo of all three. Chronic stress can even come from too much of a good thing, like running on adrenalin for long periods of time to do all the things you love like exercise, sports, or working. Overall, this type of stress leads to adrenal fatigue, even adrenal insufficiency, or crisis. What you need to know is just having Lyme or co-infections for a while leads to chronic stress in your body. Your body gets tired fighting off the invading infections and working overtime. Then you add in everyday work and relationship related stressors, and it can become a heavy burden for someone who is trying to heal from chronic illness or disease.

The key to stress being a block has to do with the levels of cortisol your body has in comparison to your DHEA. When stress is active, cortisol production is increased in the body to deal with it. DHEA is also used to counter the negative effects of the cortisol since cortisol breaks down things in your body while DHEA builds them up. Acute stress is short-lived enough that even if you use a lot of both your body goes back into a resting state and can rebuild it's stores of the stress hormones.

Now if you know someone who falls into the chronic stress category those stores are being used daily over a long period of time without much rest. This can lead to depletion of key hormones and neuro chemicals that your adrenal glands produce to keep the body functioning. This is a super simplified explanation of the chronic stress process. The main idea is that there are several essential chemicals the body needs to stay in homeostasis that change when the body is in a stress state. These can lead to blocks in healing because you will have limited ingredients to perform the functions your body normal does to stay healthy.

The good news is you can do something about this! Finding ways to put your body into a restful state and turning on the parasympathetic nervous system can greatly decrease stress or take you out of a stress state. The longer or more often you can go into this restful state, the quicker your body will be able to heal itself and restore its hormones and chemicals.

Here are some things you can do to help lower stress:

- Take a relaxing bath—use essential oils like lavender and chamomile, etc.

- Deep breathing exercises.

- Exercising for 20 minutes a day (if you are able).

- Dancing to music you like.

- Watching comedies and things that make you laugh.

- Doing things that bring you joy.

- Listening to things that make you feel happy, peaceful, joyful, or inspired.

- Being around people who bring you joy and feel good to be around.

- Set boundaries with the people in your life that tend to drain you. Say no if you don't feel up to seeing them.

- Stretching.

- Meditating.

- Taking naps.

- Laying down for 15 minutes at a time a few times a day —this can really help recharge the adrenal glands and all you have to do is find a comfy spot to recline and let your body do the rest.

- Massage.

- Therapy or counseling support.

- Taking supplements and treating infections with a doctor to bring down internal physical stressors.

- Going to bed before 10:00pm and sleeping until 7:00am or later to allow the adrenals to recharge.

- Put boundaries up at work if you find work is coming home with you too much. Make changes to how you use your time in the day.

- Cut out sugar, alcohol, caffeine (if you can), and junk foods (which can be hard since it tends to be what we crave when stressed).

- Journaling Questions to ask yourself to Identify and Decrease Stress in your Life:

- Make a list of the physical, mental, and emotional stressors in your life. Are any things you can change or decrease in some way?

- Are there any areas in your life you need to have better boundaries with friends, family, or work?

- Make a list of all the people in your life who drain your energy when you are around them – you may feel more tired or exhausted after spending time with them. Look if you need to set any boundaries with them if you want to keep them in your life. Examples could be setting time limits when you are with them or what you are up for doing with them (i.e. maybe you don't want to be in a bar but instead having tea on the couch or going for a walk at the beach while seeing them).

PART IV

Purpose Driven Living

The Summer Day

–Mary Oliver (Devotions p.316, Penguin Press, NY 2017)

Who made the world?

Who made the swan, and the black bear?

Who made the grasshopper?

This grasshopper, I mean—

the one who has flung herself out of the grass,

the one who is eating sugar out of my hand,

who is moving her jaws back and forth instead of up and down-

who is gazing around with her enormous and complicated eyes.

Now she lifts her pale forearms and thoroughly washes her face.

Now she snaps her wings open, and floats away.

I don't know exactly what a prayer is.

I do know how to pay attention, how to fall down

into the grass, how to kneel down in the grass,

how to be idle and blessed, how to stroll through the fields,

which is what I have been doing all day.

Tell me, what else should I have done?

Doesn't everything die at last, and too soon?

Tell me, what is it you plan to do

with your one wild and precious life?

30

Deep and Simple Purpose

One of the biggest gifts of dying and coming back was that suddenly everything that wasn't important fell away and I could see clearly what mattered most — relationships with people I loved. When you die you can't bring anything you own with you, no possessions, no makeup, no physical appearances, no money. What you take with you is your soul. It's that simple. Love is in everything you do and in every moment. I know many spiritual teachers like Jesus and others talk about the importance of love and it being at the core of everything. It's absolutely true.

When I died, I was sucked off the earth and onto a plane where light and energy were the foundation and communication was through pictures and super fast downloads. I had my life playing out before my eyes like you hear about from people who have had a near death experience before. But it wasn't just playing, what happened was that all my experiences, good or bad, suddenly played in one emotion — deep compassionate love for each and every person and experience I was in. There was no such thing as good or bad, the polarity and duality that we live in on Earth had fallen away. It was almost like it was a different pair of glasses I put on that allowed me to have the illusion of separateness on Earth. I had love for and felt love from my abusive stepmother who tormented me through Jr. High and High School with no one believing me at the time. I had no triggers or negative feelings come up — only love for all of it and her. I had love for everyone I saw and for myself and all that I had gone through. I wasn't thinking this was hard or bad or good - that all went away and each moment just "was". It's that simple.

After I came back into my body something else interesting happened. My nervous system that had been programmed by all of my experiences was completely reset with the frequency of love for all my memories before my re-birth. I also found that when I experienced memories from before my near death experience, I only saw the film strip pop up instead of first-person. But all my memories since my rebirth are stored and retrieved from my point of view like all my memories used to be. I also noticed that because I had no bad memories from my past I lost my sense of shame and was in a state of being "in the moment". I got to experience this for almost 3 years but around the 3rd anniversary of my near death experience I had started to rebuild some of the shame and fear as emotions. They are so minor compared to my previous 32 years of life and I am able to stay conscious and present most the time.

Here is what I found important after my near death experience and how it has changed how I live and increased wellness in my daily life.

1. I learned what was important and what wasn't. I am human, so I too can still get sucked into the trance of fretting about things society pushes as important. I now become aware of it so much faster than before which frees me to be in the moment more.

2. We are what we put ourselves around so consciously choosing what sort of things we watch or listen to can make a huge difference in our ability to heal faster.

    I was recently going through Netflix and found a documentary on Mr. Fred Rogers where he was quoted saying:

"You know, I feel so strongly that deep and simple is far more essential than shallow and complex. In the end, life isn't about material things. It's about the relationships you have with one another and yourself."

He couldn't have said more clearly what I knew inside every cell of my body when I returned to Earth. All the stuff that we entwine ourselves in like possessions, buying stuff, black and white thinking, and money are all distractions from what matters. When you die you don't take these things with you. You realize that making new connections and time and presence with those you care about is what matters. These can't be bought.

I also love the idea of being simple. Ever since I came back I knew I needed to let go of a lot of the stuff in my life — possessions were just clutter distracting me from the meaningful relationships and things I loved doing. So, when I returned home from my 3 months of recovery I started purging and simplifying my life. I watched a documentary about living as a minimalist and simplifying your life. I also read the book *The Life-Changing Magic of Tidying* by Marie Kondo. My husband and I went through every item we owned and purged about 90% of our belongings. Suddenly there was so much more space to appreciate the things that were useful because they brought us joy, a frequency that helps keep you in a healing state. We also had so much more space and time to spend on the things that mattered to us. I was able to think more clearly and start to try to learn how to write and read again, which I couldn't do for the first year after the stroke. I also could start seeing my future and meditate more easily because there was clarity and light without all the objects in our space. I didn't have to clean nearly as often. I started noticing how much energy each possession carried with it too. Some objects were energetically very heavy and I would find myself feeling more fatigued and lethargic or overwhelmed by all I needed to do. When I only had things in our living space that brought in light and were useful I felt free and lighter and healed faster. Each of these changes contributed to how I was able to heal so quickly in the bigger picture.

Living simple isn't referring just to stuff in our lives either. Living simple is becoming more conscious in our intentions in our daily behaviors. It's realizing we have the choice in what we are exposed to, who we spend time with, what we focus our attention on, and how to weed out distractions which are not in our best interest. Distractions can be many things — stuff, emotions, judgments, or shame. It can be watching or listening to things that are not in resonance with us or getting stuck on small stuff. We can jump into drama and ride the roller coaster or we can choose to keep it simple and use peace and kindness. I find it is much better for my body, mind, spirit, and healing when I find ways to keep it simple and make choices that are good for my spirit. Kindness is simple. It works and is a win-win for all involved. Simple and deep like Mr. Rogers would say. Peace is too. Love as well.

3. Meditation and grounding my body with intention allows me to have a more simple and deep day. Its super important to know yourself, be able to hear yourself, and find connection to your higher self. We are all looking for this connection and sometimes we look for it in others approval or buying more stuff, with the thought that you will feel better. The truth is being okay with our own bodies, our own souls, and loving ourselves is the most fulfilling and deep connection we can have. When we do this we can have deep and present relationships with other people too.

4. Spending time with people you love is worth more than anything money can buy. Make the time, it's what matters.

Seeing family or creating a chosen family and spending quality time together is what matters.

5. Money is not the purpose. When you find your purpose and are on the right path, money will be provided in ways you would never expect. If you focus on what your message is to the world and you share it you will find peace and joy in your heart that money can never buy. Making money is a necessity to be able to live but not the purpose.

6. Keeping clean contracts with friends and family is one of the most important jobs to have. When these are cleaned up you are able to live in the moment with direct loving communication and balance. This is simple and deep as well.

7. My relationship with spirit comes first. When I have full faith in my spirit I know I am on the right path. I get messages as images, words, or coincidences and it is very uplifting to be connected to something bigger than myself. Whatever religion or spiritual practice you come from, if it brings you closer to the light and gives you a sense of connection to God or source then that is great. I have a connection with Christ, angels, and spirit. It's different for each of us. It is a personal journey but a very important one!

Exercises, Journaling Questions, and Things to Think About

1. Simplify your life physically; take the time to go through all your stuff.

2. Watch the *Minimalism* documentary or read *The Life-Changing Magic of Tidying* by Marie Kondo.

3. As we let go of physical stuff in our lives, it also helps purge emotional baggage stored in our bodies. It's amazing how

much everything is intertwined and how much we can attach to physical stuff without realizing it.

When there was something sentimental that I wanted to remember I started taking pictures of those things and digitally saving them. If I didn't use them or look at them very often, I would say "Thank you" to the object for serving its part in my life and bringing me joy and let it go. I found that it was better to have the objects out of the house I lived in. If I let someone in the house have it I did not get the healing like I did when the object was completely out of my life. Seeing it daily in another part of the house kept me connected to it and the other person didn't usually need it. So unless it is something they can use daily it's better to let it go to a thrift store or used goods store.

4. Make a list of all the people in your life that you love. Take it to a next level and send them a card in the mail or an email or text. Expressing love and gratitude for those who are important in our lives is something money can't buy and it stays with our souls forever.

5. Make a schedule in your week and color every event where you get to interact with those you love. If your calendar has a lot of time with this color great. If it is mostly white then you may want to see what you can change in your weekly schedule to make more time for those you love. I started having Sunday lunches with my chosen family and we planned fun activities to engage with the kids — we made movies using our cell phones and had the kids direct them. It was so much fun and it allowed time for all of us to play and be present with each other. These are the memories and relationships that matter most while we are here.

6. Get your schedule back out for a week and instead of coloring time spent with those you love, color in time spent with

yourself to be quiet or introspective. Hopefully you have at least 30 minutes scheduled for this, hopefully more. This isn't being "selfish" it's giving yourself and your soul recharge time. Since we are all connected to the universal consciousness you are adding peace to the world by being in a state of peace. If you know yourself and can love yourself, then you can truly give to and love others. It also helps you center, ground, and be able to choose to live more simply like Fred Rodgers talks about.

31

You Have Purpose & You Are Loved

"Act as if what you do makes a difference. It does."

-William James

We all are loved and we all have purpose. I want you to remember this. When I was in the darkness of my own soul, lost and confused and completely hopeless, I went through many days, weeks, and months of wondering what the purpose in any of this was. Why are we here? I was so caught up in the shadows I could no longer see my own light inside. I could no longer work or do the things I thought gave me purpose in this world — I had been a middle school teacher for 15 years and worked as a therapist. I could no longer wear titles that showed I was a good caretaker in society which was how I identified my purpose in being here.

The questions began to flood in as I went from able-bodied to disabled in a few short months. Doctors had no answers and wanted to blame me for my mysterious physical breakdown which led to my mental and emotional breakdown as well. I was falling apart. Who was I when I could no longer show up in societies schedule of working 8:00am-5:00pm 5 days a week? I was just a waste - a hindrance, a user, and a burden to society, my husband, and my friends. A lot of my family and friends didn't understand what I was going through so I did not feel loved either. It was hard for me to understand how anyone could love me this way. I didn't love myself any longer. I was taking up air and space on this already overcrowded Earth. I wanted to die for the first time in my life and a few months after saying that aloud to God I did. We have choice and we are very powerful in terms of the reality we create and choose to live in — positive or negative.

But guess what? We all have purpose even when we are at our lowest low and feel like a complete failure. Yes, we still have purpose. You have to remember this. Looking back I can see now that me just being me allowed for others to have their purpose. My doctors had a patient and my husband had to go to work to take care of the wife he loved. People around town started hearing about my story and calling to get advice to help their very ill friends who had similar symptoms. A friend wanted to get a dog but having a puppy with his busy work schedule wouldn't allow him to — so he asked me to come take care of his puppy during the weekdays.

The truth is, we all need one another on Earth. We all serve a purpose and are loved. We don't have to play the role of hero to have purpose - with no villain there is no hero — and with no victim or patient there is no caretaker. It all has a balance to it. Being alive is a great big game board and we get our chance to experience all sorts of roles. If we remove the judgment about what is good or bad in society we could see we all are just playing our purpose and it is to be exactly who we are in the moment.

The movie Pollyanna is a great example. She is so optimistic and positive to strangers that it changed their lives. It helped people heal and be inspired again — her being herself and that was it, that was her purpose. She inspired others to find their light inside by shining hers.

So, remember no matter how hard you are struggling you still have purpose. A great game to play is the gladness game - no matter how awful you feel you can always find something to be glad about just like Pollyanna showed us. I dare you to try it! This is a lot of what the Dynamic Neural Retraining System (DNRS) program is about. It's about activating the limbic system in a positive way to override the negative loops and programming we can get stuck in. Remembering positive memories is another way to do this. By bringing them back to the present you are retriggering the brain chemistry of being hopeful and happy and it becomes a feeling in the now which shifts your mood to a positive one.

Want to Change your Outlook or Mood - Change your Posture!

Changing your posture changes your mood and brain chemistry. I once played this game called clay modeling where you had to take the form of an emotional event you have experienced and match the picture you had of that moment. Then another person has to get in that exact position matching you. Another person then comes over and moves that person's body around until it fully matches the person who first chose the moment to model. The last stage in this game is for the person in the pose copying the original model to guess the emotion based on the posture and expressions.

What this game teaches you is that the way we express our bodies and faces and posture directly affects our mood, outlook on life, and how we feel.

So the reverse must also be true; if we want to help ourselves shift from a darker emotion all we need to do is model someone who is in a mood we want to be in — someone happy may be smiling so we smile. When you change your posture to look up — your brain can't feel sad or depressed. Think of all the time we spend hunched over at a computer looking down — it can literally trigger depression in the brain just from the posture.

Listen, Play and Dance Away Your Blues!

For me another tool is using music as a way to change my mood. I pick one of my Pandora stations to shift my mood from angry to happy or ramped up to relaxed depending on what I want. If I am feeling low, depressed, angry, or unmotivated and am having trouble shifting out of it, I choose something really upbeat and positive and then I actually get up and move my body to it. This can be a game changer for the rest of the day.

The more joy and positivity we can connect with the more it raises our physical and energetic vibration. Positive and upbeat frequencies are similar to a wellness vibration and it is the direct way to actually put us in what's called a healing state — that's what doctors are aiming to do when they give us medications, supplements, and herbs; to shift our illness state into a healing state. Illness is when our bodies and energy fields are not resonating in a wellness frequency and its causing distress on our systems. So finding music that you can use as a tool to aid in supporting you will help yourself get better faster. This is empowering you to be your own healer and giving you easy tools that anyone can use at home or out and about.

By finding the songs and genres that resonate with your body you are helping give your body the one up it needs to continue to clear out toxins. It's a win-win for everyone around. Most importantly you.

In summary, sometimes life takes us through challenges that can feel really lonely and hard; you don't know if you can make it through. It forces you to dig deep and find who you are at the core. We sometimes try to fill ourselves up with stuff and outside interactions as distractions to not feel our discomfort when really what we need is to connect to our inner self and strength. Getting through the hard times forces us to find that inner strength and sometimes take the pause we need. We are forced to be in our bodies — the pain brings us there, the fatigue limits our ability to stay ramped up and interacting with others. We stop being able to run from ourselves and this is huge in stages of spiritual growth and healing that come from having Lyme and chronic illness.

Don't change who you are to please others.

What is purpose? What does it mean to have purpose? Do you have to make money for it to count? Do you have to "be" someone with a title or saving people in some way? We have so many beliefs and unconscious pressures form our culture and family growing up. Clearing your truth from all outside factors can sometimes be hard to figure out. I like to call this foreign energy in your space. Since we are all energy we affect each other with our thoughts and beliefs which changes our core energy.

The other day I was sitting in a kayak on the lake near my house in northern Vermont. I was having trouble with knowing I had purpose and what I should be doing next in my life. What was my purpose in being here?

As I kayaked I started to notice all the wildlife and when I returned to the dock there was a magnificent hum of frogs singing. It was one giant orchestra of loud ribbits. Then out of the corner of my eye a small frog caught my attention. It dawned on me so clearly, all this frog was supposed to do was be a frog. It was perfect just as it was, not needing to do or be anything but a frog ribbiting. That was the answer I needed! I am a human and just being alive is enough. Just being in the moment present is enough as I am. As we all are. I think we get caught up in all the shoulds and future pressures we forget that we are enough without all of that and our very presence matters just like the frogs.

So, remember, be your authentic self. Those who know you already love you as you are. Validate your core self, your strengths, natural gifts, your authentic self. Don't compromise to be liked by others. People love you as your true self and your shining light allows others to shine theirs.

32

Overwhelmed, Simplify

"Finally I saw that worrying had come to nothing. And gave it up. And took my old body and went out into the morning, and sang."

- Mary Oliver

When you feel completely overwhelmed and there is no hope any longer — remember this, think "simplicity".

When dealing with Lyme or any other chronic illness you have moments of feeling completely overwhelmed by being sick, the primary and secondary challenges that come with it, and the financial and career challenges you might face. It can feel so big and crushing that you just want to hide or give up and hope you die to get away from it all. When you find yourself here while healing from Lyme disease I want you to remember to simplify:

1. How am I right now in this moment?

2. Is there anything I can do to help myself in this moment to feel better?

3. Does my body, mind, or soul need anything specific to help myself shift this moment in some way?

4. Remind yourself that it is only a moment in time, and that moments pass and that there will be better moments soon. You

have experienced bad moments before and somehow you made it through.

All you can do is ask yourself what the right next step is and get yourself up to do it. That's it. Over time you will have accomplished 100 or 365 next steps. This is how you recover from something as big as Lyme and its co-illnesses. AA uses this philosophy too —it's going to be a marathon not a sprint! It's a new way of life to truly get back from it. Much like many alcoholics now live sober fulfilling lives, you too can recover and find your path by treating and overcoming Lyme.

Just Take It One Breath at a Time.

Another way I like to look at this is seeing breath like the steps. Living from one breath to the next. Breath is directly related to spirit; breath is life. The unseen force that fills us and keeps us alive.

Each breath has both life and death in it. The pause at the top of the breath is like death - we cease breathing for that moment and there is stillness. And in that moment there is some of the greatest potential of all. It's what makes being human so fantastic — at any given moment you can choose to start again and do things differently. You can leave the past behind, the emotions that dragged you down, and the toxic realities you bathed in and believed in, and instead choose to see the light, be in it, and radiate with it.

We have so much power. This power is in our spirit and it is a gift we are given by God. We are here to share this light and remind each other of this inner strength. When you choose to use it for good, great joy and purpose are found. We want to live, but when you are feeling so sick that you can't get out of bed or contribute, you can lose touch with this inner strength and forget who you are; that you are powerful beyond measure and able to heal yourself when you ask the higher powers that be.

33

Lessons fron My Journey with Lyme

"Storms make trees take deeper roots."

- Dolly Parton

Overcoming the Depression, Hopelessness, and the Inner Darkness of Chronic Illness

So, I had Lyme and chronic illness, now what? How do I restart my life? Where do I start? Does it even matter? What's the purpose in any of this? We all die in the end anyway!

I found it was important for me to make sense of my feelings around having an illness that stopped my life in its tracks and sent me on a completely different path than I had planned. You go through the stages of grief having to let go of your "old life" before you got sick, your expectations for what you were going to be and do, and you have to grieve and let go of the old you. Then, more importantly, you must embrace a new path and future. Find gratitude for what you have learned and how you have grown from the experiences you have gone through. Accept and come up with accommodations for your new weaknesses by identifying your new abilities and strengths. What are your new gifts now? What are your passions and is there a new purpose for you in your life?

I went through ups and down as I continued to heal from Lyme. I still am! I would have times when I felt totally overwhelmed, hopeless, lost, and confused about the meaning of it all. These times were dark but they usually didn't last long and I found they helped me dig deep and find what was important to me. I went from believing that when I grew up I would get married, have a career I was passionate about, have kids, a house, and I would know what to do each day. That the American Dream would just happen and I could always just push myself to get things done and have unlimited energy for doing things I wanted to do.

Then Lyme hit and most of that was shattered. My type A personality that loved to be busy could no longer sustain due to the crippling fatigue. My body hurt and ached and wouldn't work in ways I asked it to anymore. I couldn't get pregnant due to my health being such a mess and my stress tolerance was so low carrying a baby would have been dangerous for my adrenals. Our house was sold to pay off medi-cal bills — bye-bye white picket fence. Lyme flipped my entire idea of what a successful life looked like on its head! It didn't stop there but shook it until everything else fell out. I was a tossed salad and I was confused on what life was all about and how I could ever be "success-ful" again. My definition of "able" was insane. It required working 16 plus hours a day, burning the candle both ends. I was a teacher for 15 years and it required working outside all the time. I was working with emails and prep before and after school hours, constantly fielding calls from parents and the school dealing with other's problems. It was so rewarding and fun while I was healthy but when I couldn't do it any longer I just felt like a complete failure, hopeless for any sort of mean-ingful future since teaching was what I had wanted to do since I was 3 years old. That part of me had died when I had the stroke and near death experience. It was gone. I was reborn with a completely differ-ent set of skills and purpose and that shift doesn't happen overnight. It's a process. I just kept asking myself what is the purpose of it all? Why am I still here if I can't do all the things I used to? I was judging myself to my old abilities which were not that balanced or healthy for my whole body and soul anyways.

> *"It's no use going back to yesterday*
> *because I was a different person then."*

- Lewis Carroll, Alice's Adventures in Wonderland

The story about my experience on the lake last summer with the frogs, where I realized their life purpose is to be a frog, kept me thinking *why isn't that enough for us as humans? To just be alive and present in each moment?* By being present we can be there for each other and the opportunities that exist right in front of us. That is enough. We don't know how we affect others in our path - small interactions can make huge differences in other lives. Trusting that the universe has bigger plans and being present allows us to be vehicles of those lessons for each other. If we are too busy on "our" plan of what our purpose is, sometimes we can miss opportunities that are right in front of us. How many times have you been in the grocery store and then back at your car without really remembering all you did because you were so lost in your own busy thoughts about what you needed to be doing? You may have walked right by multiple opportunities for connections laid out for you right there in the grocery store. That's what I have been trying to be better at since having Lyme. Being aware of those around me and being present in the moment without feeling like I need to be "doing" all the time.

When we find ourselves with new health challenges or physical limitations that make us "disabled" we can become depressed, lost, and hopeless. Our society pushes us to be something bigger and better every day; success is propelling yourself forward at all cost. Now that you are unable to push and ramp up, where is your place in our culture? What is your role? Are you just a waste of space? How do you have the right to be alive? You might feel shame in resting, in taking care of yourself, in being still. In other cultures, stillness is taught and accepted — mediation and retreat are practiced and encouraged. They see the value in being in stillness, the productiveness that comes from stopping to listen. Sometimes we get so busy we are actually creating more chaos and drama than there needs to be. We are not being successful but more like a chicken running around with its head chopped off. How is that healthy? Being on a journey of healing gives you the gift of waking up and figuring out and redefining what success, limits, purpose, and life all mean to you. It isn't a familiar feeling and takes some deep diving to change inside you. One great thing I have noticed is I am often in a state of peace since I went through all this. There isn't much that can rock me emotionally or physically because I know I can get through it and that I don't have to compare myself to anyone else, especially to our culture of being "too busy!" Instead I can laugh and smile and stay in the moment because I don't believe it's what my purpose is any more.

Love is All that Matters.

I see everything from my first life with no judgment but amusement and pure love for all I was involved with.

Love is all we take with us, not stuff, money, or fame. So let all the ego, shame, and worry go and be here now. Live. Focus on love and finding ways to share and experience love every day. All the other things are distractions from being here fully. Spending time with those you love and cleaning up contracts with them each day is important. This is soul work and it goes with you when you die unlike your physical stuff. Make time for it, because it matters.

Decluttering the Soul through Letting Go of Your Stuff

Having less stuff and more time and clarity is important.. About 6 months into recovering from the stroke of Lyme I watched a documentary called Minimalism that was just released at the time. I had always enjoyed cleaning and reorganizing my bedroom growing up. I liked the sense of control and creativity I could express in changing my space just by changing the furniture and decorations. I always felt like my brain was my bedroom - if my room was messy, so was my ability to concentrate and do things in my life. Having ADHD,

I learned that keeping my room clean and organized helped me get way more done in my daily life without messing up deadlines. My bedroom was a direct reflection of my mind.

When I got Lyme I couldn't keep up on my living space. Cleaning took every bit of energy I had and I couldn't focus long enough to finish or get the feeling of reward I used to. It was just work.

As I watched *Minimalism,* for the first time I realized it was what I needed to do to heal this area of my life with Lyme. I needed to let go of a lot of my "stuff", and in doing this I would be also letting go of emotional "stuff" that was attached to the items.

Now that I was sick, one thing that happened was I was much more vulnerable to energies around me. All the stuff I had collected in my space had energy attached to it. Old memories, emotions, other people's energy, etc... Every time I was in my room I was picking up on all these energies that used to bring me comfort but now over-whelmed me because I couldn't filter it out as background energy. My space was cluttered. My energy field was cluttered with old energies from other people in my life. It happens to all of us. So I began the process of decluttering my space by aiming to become a minimalist like the documentary shared. I did it in very small steps, starting with my closet and going through my clothes. If I didn't use it regularly and if it didn't bring me joy when I looked at it I put it in the bag to be given away to the thrift store. The most amazing thing happened; as I let go of things I felt my own body getting lighter and I started to find I was more able to recharge in my space again. My room was becom-ing my energy - healthy and clear of all the other energies, as loving as they may have been. Their energy was not my energy frequency, so it was a distracting force in my room.

I shared my room with my husband, Adam, so he joined me in the task of decluttering. He cleared his stuff and I cleared mine and we found that it also increased our love for each other with all the extra "stuff" out of the way. It created great conversations about what we were letting go of inside of us that we didn't even know was there. I learned that by decluttering my physical life, I was decluttering my soul as well. It made a huge shift in how fast I was able to heal — one of the things that propelled me forward on my journey to light! I had always found joy in cleaning and organizing but I had never learned that clearing out and letting go of things was an even bigger reward than just cleaning. Plus, with less stuff I spent so much less time and energy having to clean my space because there was less to wipe down, move, or set up. Less stuff, more time! Time is the most precious commodity we have and I want to spend it on things that really matter to me, even if that's just having the extra 10 minutes to meditate and connect to my soul each day instead of cleaning. Or having 10 minutes to go for a walk or talk to a friend or family member.

I encourage you to try this if you haven't. It is an amazingly freeing experience and can become quite addictive as you begin learning how to let go of stuff and see how much lighter you feel in other areas of your life.

Film to Watch:

Minimalism: A Documentary About the Important Things, 2015, 1h 19m. It is free to watch on Netflix and is available on other streaming sites as well.

34

Finding Your New Identity

"We must be willing to let go of the life we planned so as to have the life that is waiting for us."

- Joseph Campbell

Finding Your New Identity

Happy Re-Birth-day!

You will go through a rebirthing process as you heal from Lyme, grieving the old you and recognizing its not the end, but the beginning! You get to create who you are in a way that is healthy and balanced for you *now* as you are in *this moment*.

Stop comparing your old self to your new self. Do it once in the grieving process, make a list of those things you felt defined who you were - what you were able to do in a day, a week, a month, etc, and then thank it, burn it, and let it go! Start fresh. Make a list of the things you can do today, *as you are.* The things you give to others just by being alive and you, and how you help the world just by being you.

Make the conscious choice to fill your days up doing things that matter to your soul and purpose. But how do you know what those things are? Ask yourself what lights me up? What makes me excited about waking up and doing? Once you are aware of what your passions are then you can choose what you spend your time and energy on, it matters! Life is short! Your passions and interests are there as guides to get you to do your purpose, to be you! That is what you are here for. Make time for those things and do them! And while you are having fun and doing what you love, you will find that you will attract others on their path and inspire each other in meaningful ways. That is what we are all here to do. To learn and connect in intimate ways to grow as humans and souls.

Journaling Reflection Questions

1. Identify the "voices" - the "shoulds" society and people around you have put on you.

2. Make a list of what the culture you live in says you should be or do.

3. Ask yourself what are the roles given to me in my family and social groups? Care taker? Martyr? Hero? Victim? Persecutor? Rescuer? Leader? Follower? Do these roles fit who you feel you are inside or want to be?

4. Am I doing things that exhaust me physically to save others? Emotionally? Mentally?

5. What is my motivation in doing those things that do not bring me joy or fulfillment in my life?

6. What is my motivation in pushing myself to the point of exhaustion?

7. Make a list of all those things or people that you feel drained around or after being near.

8. What is it that causes me to feel energetically drained, is there anything I can do to rebalance that?

9. What are things that give me energy?

10. What helps me recharge?

11. What are my passions?

12. What brings me joy?

13. What is beautiful to me?

14. What do I believe the purpose of life is? Am I living in alignment with these beliefs?

15. What recharges my soul so I can be healthy and bring wellness to the world?

16. What goals or things do I want to experience in life? My bucket list?

17. Is there a subject or topic you want to learn about? Any classes or workshops you have wanted to take but put off? This is a great time to try and learn new things. If you are too sick right now, at least recognizing what you still want to learn about in the future can help build more motivation in your healing. Plus learning new things helps the brain rewire and heal from Lyme as well. Win-win! Fun and healing!

35

Enough, Brings Joy

*"Instructions for living a life: pay attention. Be astonished.
Tell about it."*

- Mary Oliver

Let me share this excerpt from a book that I feel sums up the idea of being enough well.

"JOHN BOGLE, the founder of Vanguard who passed away in 2019, once told a story about money that highlights something we don't think about enough:

At a party given by a billionaire on Shelter Island, Kurt Vonnegut informs his pal, Joseph Heller, that their host, a hedge fund manager, had made more money in a single day than Heller has earned from his widely popular novel *Catch-22* over its whole history. Heller responds, "Yes, but I have something he will never have... enough."

Enough. I was stunned by the simple eloquence of that word - stunned for two reasons: first, because I have been given so much in my own life and, second, because Joseph Heller couldn't have been more accurate.

For a critical element of our society, including many of the wealthiest and most powerful among us, there seems to be no limit today on what enough entails." - Morgan Housel (*The Psychology of Money*).

Money isn't the answer. It is needed to live and for basic needs to be met but having lots of it doesn't equate to you being happy or better than.

In freshman year of college I found myself in a bit of a depression. I decided I would ride my bike across America with my best friend Lila for the summer, leave the university I was attending and take some time to think while pedaling my booty 3500 miles. Little did I know that the true education I would get would be from the small group of adults Lila and I got paired with at the start of our trip. We had decided to sign up with Adventure Cycling to have some other adults to share the experience and so we didn't have to plan the route or where we were staying each night. We were self-contained, carrying all our gear on our bikes and camping in parks throughout the trip. We had no car support, but we had a leader to guide us in terms of where we were going each day.

We arrived to meet our group for the summer and found that all the other riders were over 60 and newly retired from a lifetime of careers and hard work. They were signing up for this trip as a reward for their years of working. We didn't think much of this at the time but we both came to find that there was a heaviness that had settled into much of the group as they realized that just because they retired didn't mean life was going to be easy. The truth was, they were still who they were. They were still unhappy, jaded, and now extra resentful because they were starting to realize that all those things they thought would come with retirement — ease, relaxation, time — wasn't all just given to them. In reality it was with them their entire lives. They believed they couldn't have it if they were going to be successful adults making lots of money. They were telling themselves that once they retired life would be all they imagined... all the hard work would pay off. But in reality the work that had not been done was on themselves where these stresses actually originated.

It made me more aware that I needed to live my life starting now, not in the future. Making sure where I chose to spend most of my time each day fulfilled my soul and passions, not just as a way to make money as a job or work. It had to include play and fun in it as well and connection with people at a heart level in some way. Even in writing books now I feel as though I am sitting on my couch having intimate conversations with the reader. It is very fulfilling to my soul to spend time doing this and it's a lot of fun!

When I had the near death and Lyme my challenges and experiences only reinforced my lessons from that summer crossing America. I realized more and more, especially as we lost income from medical bills, that we always had enough. I learned that when you have a lot you sometimes start to get distracted by the fear of losing it. When we were at our poorest, living in a tent in someone's backyard, only months after the stroke, we found that there is a gift in realizing you don't necessarily need more to still have joy in your life. It makes me think of visiting countries in Africa where I saw so much joy in people who literally had nothing in terms of monetary worth. I am not saying having money is a bad thing by any means. What I am sharing is the realization that money isn't the end-all and it isn't going to bring you joy in your future, unless you are already joyful inside yourself.

I also realize that time and money are an exchange. Time is precious. We are alive now and not guaranteed tomorrow, so essentially when you go to work and get paid you are getting paid for your time. It is an exchange. Time to me is so valuable I have to be doing things I love and are in line with my purpose of helping others to find joy in the money I receive as a trade. Otherwise I find I become burnt out if I am only doing work to make the money. I am more likely to crash health-wise which ends up costing more in bills than it was worth to make. When I am doing things in alignment with my purpose the money comes in and it's always enough. I am not resentful for it in any way and that is priceless to my soul. I also find that those who make a lot money are doing things they creatively designed from their passions. They aren't focused on the money they are making, but more so on the fun they can have creating and that is enough. So do things that matter most to you, that align with your purpose and passions, and money will come in some way or shape most likely.

36

Detachment, Free Will and the Power to Heal

"The laws of Detachment:
Allow others to be who they are.
Allow yourself to be who you are.
Don't force situations. Solutions will emerge.
Uncertainty is reality-embrace it."

-Sue Fitzmaurice

Throughout my healing journey, I had to realize I needed help letting go of control of those I loved and worried about.

I learned a great way to look at the idea of detachment from Pam Oslie, a spiritual counselor, that actually clicked and made sense to me at my core. She said to me, "Caroline, you have to trust that their soul knows what it is doing." It was that simple.

I was continuing to unconsciously tell my family members that I did not trust their soul knew what it was doing, which I realize wasn't true. I was trying to play God, to control things that were not in my control. I may not have trusted them as humans, but at a soul level I knew they had their path to walk and it wasn't mine to dictate or control. We are just two souls sharing parts of each others paths when we interact, but we are still on our own unique journey in time and space.

I had to use this with family members who were using substances and I had no control over stopping them even when I tried. I would stress myself out because I was so fearful of losing them. Pam helped me see it in a new light and helped diffuse the amount of stress I was creating inside myself so that I could be more present in my life and give my family members back responsibility for their own.

I found that if I believe in the other person's soul and its higher knowing, then I can trust it knows what it is doing. It becomes so much easier to let it go! I can detach from the outcome, allowing that person's soul space to learn what it is meant to. I can send a prayer out for their safety and wellbeing but that's it.

Another way I could say it is I trust in God's path for this person.

In letting go, it doesn't mean I have to cut the person out of my life. On the contrary I found I had more compassion for them and I was more present to be available when they were ready for help. I let them know I would be there if they needed anything in the future, that I didn't agree with their choice to drink and use drugs, and that I genuinely loved them and was worried about them. But I wasn't going to be around them any longer when they were drinking or using for my own health. I set a clear and loving boundary but also kept a door open to be there when they were ready. I was no longer enabling them by rescuing them in their daily lives. I would feel guilty or like I was being mean by having boundaries around this. Once I understood that I truly trust in their soul knowing what it is doing, I was able to detach and let my fear go. In trade I got to let the stress go!

Taking Responsibility For What IS Ours, Our Healing!

My brother was drinking alcohol a lot and for years I tried everything I could to get him to stop and see how destructive it was. I finally got that I had to trust his soul knew what it was doing and that he was here to learn what he was learning. It was not my responsibility or job to do it for him. I was able to let go of a huge weight on my shoulders because I could see that it was part of his journey on Earth, just like

I had lessons to learn from getting Lyme disease. In a few years times he had figured out that he didn't like how he felt on alcohol, that he was losing everything he loved, and he made the change from a place of desire to be better for himself.

This is the only way he would stop anyways — it had to come from him. Only he could heal himself and ask for the help when he was ready just like I believe only you can heal you from chronic illness and Lyme — no doctor or anyone else. It is your journey and your responsibility. You are in charge of getting your team made to support you in the journey to whole health and recovery. You are the one who asks for help from God or from people around you. No one else can do it for you. It's your soul's journey.

I also believe in the body's deep desire to heal itself — it's programmed and designed to do it. It just needs help sometimes to reach homeostasis so the systems can work the way they are designed to.

I trust in my body and talk to it and tell it how thankful I am for all it is doing to keep me well and get me back to wellness. I used to thank my liver, spleen, and colon for all they do to keep me healthy. I would tell them that the enema I was doing was their chance to release toxins quickly and easily. I would thank God for the amazingly strong and complex body I was given. Gratitude for my body was huge in my healing process with Lyme.

I talked to the infections in my body as well. I told them they were not welcome and needed to leave gently and easily. I told them my immune system was working very well and would find them and kill them if they did not leave right now. Just like in those experiments where they looked at water molecules under the microscope, by speaking to our bodies we begin to shift the water in us to higher cleaner frequencies. Why not? You've got nothing to lose but maybe sounding a little crazy talking to yourself in the bathroom.

37

The Power of Asking for Help

"Knock and it will be opened for you."

- Matthew 7:7

When you are chronically sick for a long time you learn that you sometimes need help. It can be hard to ask for help for some of us. A huge lesson I learned while going through my healing journey was the power of asking for help, and not just help from the earthly plain. What was most amazing is when you ask, help tends to be given fairly quickly. It may not always be exactly how you imagined but help will follow, sometimes better than you would have even thought to ask for.

Earthly Plane Help

First, I want you to know it is okay to ask for help from others. We are all on Earth together having these experiences and in asking you are also giving the opportunity for someone else to give to you. Think of times when you have offered to help another and they said yes. You usually felt really good about whatever it was you did for them. You got to share in a relationship of caring. If that person wasn't open to receiving the help, that exchange would have never taken place. Those are the types of interactions that we remember and take into our souls as meaningful. If you are used to being more of a caretaker, which a lot of chronically ill people tend to be, this is God's gift to you; to learn to receive and give someone else the chance to learn what it feels like to give. You are still giving to the other person by allowing them to help you.

For me it really helped to see how both sides of the interaction are equally important and rewarding. I wasn't weak, needy, or unworthy by asking for help. It was just the opposite, it took courage to say what I needed from another because there's no certainty that they will say yes. You feel vulnerable putting yourself on the spot, this is what allows the other person to experience what it feels like to be compassionate and caring if they are not used to being the one taking care of you. It's a beautiful gift if you let it be.

Also asking for help from people you may not know well or even a stranger tends to be an amazing way to let someone in on a deeper level, getting to connect with the world around you, and create positive energy from the transaction. A frequency of love comes from it! This helps you and the others involved in helping you heal.

Prayer: Help from Above and Beyond

Secondly, I learned that if I trusted in the higher powers that be and asked for heavenly help from God, he always came through and answered me. This ended up being more powerful than I could ever imagine. I think I was listening to a podcast about angels when I first even thought about asking for help outside of the earthly plane. I decided to try what the podcaster was speaking about and I asked God to come and help me get through the last 5% of the Lyme treatment. The first 90% was quicker, the last 10% lingered for two years. I was feeling overwhelmed and tired from being sick so long and still getting the same results on testing. I still remember exactly where I was, pushing the lawn mower in our back yard, and I started talking to God. I almost laughed at myself because it felt so ridiculous at the time. But I decided to go for it and ask God and the angels for help. I felt myself fully surrender and genuinely ask from my heart as I went on mowing and weeding and doing my earthly duties as usual.

A week later, I had completely forgotten about the prayer I had put out there, but I had a follow up blood test and bioenergetic testing to see where I was at with the Lyme. I had done nothing differently from the previous check ins, so I wasn't expecting much of a change. The results came back from bioenergetic testing first. "Caroline I don't know what you did but the Lyme is no longer showing up as a stressor in your body. That is pretty amazing!" A week later my blood results came back. Guess what?! They showed I was clear of all Lyme for the first time in 3 years. I still had a few co-infections lingering but the Lyme was gone!

I sat there dumbfounded. It hit me that it is exactly what I had asked for help with and it was received. From that day on I believed in the power of prayer, God, and of angels. I began to ask for help with all sorts of things to see how it all worked and gave praise and gratitude for all I received. It wasn't just the process of asking and receiving, but I believe I was switching my own energetic field to say yes, I am worthy and deserving of receiving things I need. This gave me a frequency that attracts more of what I am needing into my life. Before I couldn't even see it to accept it. I had blinders up — "NO world, I can do this on my own. I don't need help. I can give help but not receive it because that is weak." I am so thankful for having such a bad case of Lyme disease when I did because it ended up leading me to God and spiritual growth in ways I would have never sought without my challenges getting as bad as they were. It broke me down and made me vulnerable and humbled me in ways I would have never allowed myself to become if I hadn't been so sick. I never wish hardship or illness on anyone, but if you are dealt that card or have invited that experience in then I am excited for all the gifts and growth that come from it in the end. Having faith in the unknown and trusting by asking and letting go of the result took away some of the blocks I had hit. God had ways outside of this reality to heal me or get me what I needed without me "doing" all the time. When we are overwhelmed or tired sometimes those two feelings can feel far away or like work to find. The good news is the more you do it the easier it is to stay in a frequency of gratitude and love. This in return begins to heal you on its own just by shifting your frequency from the outside in.

Just remember:

You are worth it. You deserve it. You are loved. Ask for help anytime.

"Afoot and lighthearted I take to the open road, healthy, free, the world before me."

-Walt Whitman

References

Books

Diamond, John. Your Body Doesn't Lie. Warner Books, 1979.

Sparks, Laurance. Self-hypnosis: A Conditioned Response Technique. Wilshire Book Company, 1962.

Hartmann, Thom. *Walking Your Blues Away: How to Heal the Mind and Create Emotional Well-Being.* Park Street Press, 2006

Hay, Louise L. *Heal Your Body: The Mental Causes for Physical Illness and the Metaphysical Way to Overcome Them.* 4th edition, Hay House, 1982.

Wilson, James L. *Adrenal Fatigue: The 21st Century Stress Syndrome.* Smart Publications, 2001.

Virtue, Doreen. *Healing With the Angels.* Hay House, 1999.

Grandin, Temple. *Thinking in Pictures: My Life With Autism.* 2nd edition, Vintage Books, 2006.

Fossum, Merie A, and Marilyn, Mason J. *Facing Shame: Families in Recovery.* W. W. Norton & Company Ltd, 1986.

Oslie, Pamela. *Infinite You: A Journey to Your Greater Self and Beyond.* Oslie Press, 2013.

Hopper, Annie. *Wired for Healing: Remapping the Brain to Recover from Chronic and Mysterious Illnesses.* The Dynamic Neural Retraining System, 2014.

O'Bryan, Tom. *You Can Fix Your Brain.* Rodale Books, 2018.

Menendex Cepero, Silvia A, and Weiser, Mark T. *Advances of Ozone Therapy in Medicine and Dentistry.* 2016.

Shoemaker, Ritchie C. *Surviving Mold: Life in the Era of Dangerous Buildings.* Otter Bay Books, 2010.

Loggins, Julia. *Dare to Detoxify.* Vibrant Health Publishing, 2012.

Housel, Morgan. *The Psychology of Money: Timeless lessons on wealth, greed, and happiness.* Harriman House, 2020.

Websites

Lyme Catalyst Section

Osborne, Jackie. "Ascension Symptoms." *The Open Spirit,* https://www.theopenspirit.com/ascension-symptoms.html.

Enema Section – Cheese craving Neurotransmitters

Rowlan, Michael P. "This Is Your Brain On Cheese." *Forbes,* https://www.forbes.com/sites/michaelpellmanrowland/2017/06/26/cheese-addiction/#2a7440f63583

Sauna Section

Bauer, Brent A. "What is an infrared sauna? Does it have health benefits?" *Mayo Clinic,* https://www.mayoclinic.org/healthy-lifestyle/consumer-health/expert-answers/infrared-sauna/faq-20057954

"Radiant-75-in-H-x-35-25-in-W-x-35-75-in-D-Hemlock-Fir-Wood." *Lowes*, https://www.lowes.com/pd/Radiant-75-in-H-x-35-25-in-W-x-35-75-in-D-Hemlock-Fir-Wood/1000044273

Radiant Saunas. "Radiant Saunas Single Person Indoor Portable FAR Infrared Sauna with Remote Control." *Wayfair*, https://www.wayfair.com/Radiant-Saunas—Salem-1-Person-FAR-Infrared-Sauna-BSA6310-L3531-K-RDA1045.html?refid=GX444197840613-RDA1045&device=c&ptid=331457627415&network=g&targetid=pla-331457627415&channel=GooglePLA&ireid=41709459&fdid=1817&gclid=CjwKCAjwz6_8BRBkEiwA3p02VbFIZd8A77SW4mQtbOrmv6PZabDj0CySb5A6KLStjkiku1ooqDzG4xoC-jYQAvD_BwE

SereneLife. "SereneLife AZSLISAU10BK Infrared Home Spa One Person Sauna with Heating Foot Pad and Portable Chair, Black." *Amazon*, https://www.amazon.com/gp/product/B079QXK2TQ/ref=ppx_yo_dt_b_search_asin_title?ie=UTF8&psc=1

DNRS and BRAIN TAP

Hopper, Annie. *DNRS: Dynamic Neural Retraining System*, https://retrainingthebrain.com

Brain Tap, https://braintap.com

"Emotions: limbic system." *Khan Academy*, https://www.khanacademy.org/test-prep/mcat/processing-the-environment/emotion/v/emotions-limbic-system

Ozone Section

PurO3, https://shop.puro3.com

Longevity Resources, https://www.ozonegenerator.com

Mast Cell

"Do I Have Mast Cell Activation Syndrome (MCAS)?" *Franklin Cardiovascular Associates*, https://franklincardiovascular.com/do-i-have-mast-cell-activation-syndrome-mcas

Other

Minimalism: A Documentary About the Important Things. Directed by Matt D'Avella, Catalyst, 2015.

Acknowledgments

I want to thank all those who played a conscious or unconscious role in my healing journey from 2015-2020.

A special thanks to my healing team:

Naturally intuitive integrative specialist in mold and infectious diseases Dr. Rajan Patel, MD for leading me on my path to recovery and for guiding me to overcome and treat the Lyme disease and mold illness I faced. You were nothing but kindness and support through it all. You taught me the power of less is more and how strong lower doses can be in treating illnesses and guided me on what to look at in my life on a soul and emotional level and how it related to my physical health. Thank you for being so safe and trustworthy for me to be myself with and heal. Special thanks to Suzy Malek at your office as well for always being there and responding so quickly with love and clarity;

Naturopath and Bioenergetic Healing Practitioner Treya Palmer for teaching me the power of intention in healing and how the energy body and spirit relates to the physical body. You were such a strong force in my healing journey. You helped open my heart to new levels and become the person I am today wanting to be of service to others with chronic illness and challenges helping them find the light like you helped me find. You believed I could heal and would heal and that belief was contagious and I began to believe it too, and that's when I really started healing faster. Thank you for all you did for me and so many others you worked with who had Lyme and Chronic Illnesses;

Dedicated and compassionate therapist John Fox, LMFT for teaching me all that I know about mental and emotional wellness and guiding me through the post traumatic stress triggers I got throughout my journey with Lyme. You supported me during the diagnosis process and encouraged me to not give up, keep looking for answers, and build and find the healing team that I did. I went through a lot of doctors who wanted to tell me it was all in my head, and without you telling me it wasn't I may have given up and not ever gotten treated for the Lyme disease I had. So thank you. You brought humor to my experiences as well. Laughter heals;

Supportive and gentle integrative wellness and Lyme disease specialist Dr. Jennifer Salcido, ND for teaching me through experience to trust my intuition and in how much the body can tell what it wants or needs in treatments through using specialized forms of bioenergtic testing. You were always available when I was in fear or had some new scary feeling symptoms while treating the Lyme and would find easy solutions and supplements to support my body with the shifts as I healed from the Lyme disease and co-infections. You are a safe space and non-judging of those who seek your help, a quality that can be hard to find when you are dealing with Lyme disease. Thank you for being there always;

Engineer and Quantum Healer Paul Tom for teaching me through experiencing the power of imagination and intention in healing, more thanks coming in a future book about my healing journey from lung cancer this last year in which you played an even bigger role in helping save my life;

Charlotte Gilchrist Energy Balancing and Nutrition specialist for teaching me through experience how outside energies from the people around me and old emotions can get stuck in my body and energy field and how to rebalance them. These old frequencies can block the flow of healing in my physical body. Thank you for doing the clearings with me and teaching me how to do them on myself as I became well and stronger. You taught me tools to shift my frequency when I knew it was off into a state of healing and out of "stuckness" or illness through working with my higher self, using meditation, through sound therapy, through imagination and conscious intention, and nutrition. Thank you;

Thoughtful ozone therapy specialist Dr. Jonathon Birch, ND teaching me all about the power of ozone to heal and for doing much needed treatments with me;

Tahara Ezrahti from Applied Intuition for teaching me how to ground energetically and create a stronger auric field boundary so I can filter the sensory world better and not be so overwhelmed and much more;

Colon hydrotherapy guru and expert Julia Loggins opening my doors to healing through colon cleansing;

Dr. Robert Mathis for always being there for me when I needed tests run or when I ended up in the hospital. You were one of the best general practitioners I had and oversaw all my treatments supportive of my choices in who I added to my health team and open to new treatment options. You saved my life while in the hospital making sure I received the care I needed when doctors missed what was going on with me;

Chiropractor Dr. Weston, for teaching me the importance of having an aligned and healthy spine and posture. When I started with you it was the last year of my healing journey from Lyme to light and I knew I was missing something in all the treatments and support I was getting. I got that I still had Lyme and its infections and toxins hiding in my spine and it was one of the last things I needed to address. You worked with me on an integral chiropractic program coming 1-4 times a week for adjustments and exercises and as we went through the stages I went through new extinction bursts of Lyme and its toxins being released from my spine as he adjusted it. After we finished that year plan I felt a huge difference in my neurological symptoms and a lot lighter from having found most of what was left hiding in my tissues and joints by manipulating them and treating the Lyme with medicine and supplements with my doctors at the same time. Having clear communication from our brains to our nervous system in our whole body is crucial for sustained wellness and circulation. Thank you;

Evan's Relaxation Station in Santa Barbara for the amazing walk in massages whenever I needed them to increase circulation, detoxification, and healing;

Alan and Anita at the Santa Barbara Center for Lymphatic Health for teaching me about the importance of supporting the lymphatic system and how to do it;

Special thanks to my family and chosen family members;

Adam Taft, Alicia Lopez, Camilla La Mer, John DeLoreto, RJ DeLoreto, Edward DeLoreto, who has always supported me, Pam Boswell, Kiaora Fox, Monique Franco, Silvia Beidermann, Ferman Kelly Jr III, Rachel Sarah Thurston, Scott Fitzstephens, The Fox-Kovach's, Katy Jacobson, Santa Barbara Middle School, Suzanne Prince, Teresa Jamison, Jay Fortman, Audrey Palmer, Shelley Greenbaum, Lila Ferguson, Crosby Buhl, Eric Lehman, Maureen Hazard Lehman, Ellen Anderson, Rachel Thurston, Wendelin Wagner, Jen Slemp, Chris Lathem, Kimmy, and so many others! I am sorry if I am missing you… There are so many I am thankful for helping me on this healing journey so know you are loved and appreciated if you don't see your name here and you were part of my journey. Thank you!!!

And special thanks to and remembrance of my grandpa James DeLoreto who passed on May 29, 2017. He was always supportive and understanding of the challenging journey with Lyme I was going through when others in my family didn't understand or believe Lyme existed so had trouble knowing how to treat me. You never turned your back on me and showed me nothing but love and concern. You told me through your actions on an unconscious level that I had worth and value, and that I was loved. I will always remember your kindness; support both emotionally and financially, your love and compassion for me through it all. Your unconditional love and sense of humor about life helps me continue to want to be here and help others know they are loved with or without Lyme too. I love you and miss you each day.

Thanks for writing support from:

To my mom, Camilla La Mer, who is constantly engaging my mind with her abundant creativity. You help me think outside the box and have fun creating my books with your freedom to express yourself in all you do my whole life. Thank you for coming out to Vermont and helping me through the editing process of the book so I could get it finished! You understand my learning disabilities and help clean my writing up without changing my voice or what I was trying to say. Thank you! Love you;

To Rachel Sarah Thurston for being my writing cheerleader, friend, and inspiration with our weekly zooms throughout COVID-19 shutdown and for being a huge force of compassionate support from your own experiences in life with health stuff. You helped bring humor to it all so it was easier to get through! You are a true lifetime friend that I am blessed to have in my life;

To Uncle Edward DeLoreto, you were the first person to read my rough draft of this entire book. I was so touched that you took the time and interest to learn more about my journey and to support me. You have been a crucial support in my health and healing over the years and I am thankful to have you in my life as family. I love you;

To Margie Dunki-Jacobs for being the amazing inspiring friend and coach getting me unstuck and back on the train writing.

To Shelley Greenbaum for your time, support, and care whilst I was writing this book and recovering from Lyme. I love you.

To my partner Adam for making me hot chocolates and green teas and reminding me to sit down and write! And for helping me edit the finished draft. So helpful! I love you;

To Dawn Densmore-Parent who helped me brainstorm and work through my blocks in writing this. Your insight and guidance has been precious and I thank God everyday for you being in my life. I wouldn't have finished this without your support and encouragement. Thank you;

To Julian Dean, Clear Path Counsel, for helping me navigate my new brain and life a few months after my near death experience. He inspired me to start writing this book page by page, one word st a time, when my brain wasn't working enough to keep track of the bigger picture. He had so much compassion and deep personal understanding of what I had gone through and helped me make sense of all of it. A gift from heaven.

To Karen Scheffler, owner and creator of Catalyst Coffee Bar in Saint Albans, VT for being my "office" for writing this book each day and supplying me amazing creative drinks to focus and relax through the process. Thanks for the laughter and smiles each day! (www.catalystcoffeebar.com)

To Christine Gail for her coaching and encouragement. And thanks to Shiloh Schroeder for the Interior Layout and her care and time. Thank you for being so understanding with all the unexpected challenges that came up in the process to get this book done;

A special thanks to and remembrance to my dad, John DeLoreto, who passed away June 17, 2022 while I was finishing the book, Thank you for gifting me for my 36th birthday the Unleash Your Rising Author Program so I could make this dream a reality with the help of an accountability coach. Also thank you for all your financial support the last year of my Lyme treatment to be able to do some of the things I had waited on doing due to financial hardship. They helped me fully recover and get to where I am today. Thank you for the support. I love you.

From Lyme to Light Book Series

This series has been created to show how Lyme disease is a catalyst for change from lower density living to higher frequency spiritual evolvement and development and to help empower you on your healing journey. The series is here to help you with your whole body healing from Lyme with examples and invitations to explore Lyme in new ways.

In 2016 I had a near-death after a stroke from neurological Lyme disease that completely changed my life path and the way I saw the world. I was given a clear message of my new purpose coming back to Earth and the gift of seeing that we are all energy and frequency, and **so are** our illnesses and health challenges.

In this book, *From Lyme to Light* the first of the series, I will share about how Lyme disease is changing those that have it from the inside out, literally - physically, emotionally, energetically, and spiritually if they want it or not. If you are going to successfully overcome and heal from Lyme disease it forces you to look at all sides of healing. I will introduce you to my **"Diamond of Healing Model"** aiming to explain the emotional, mental, physical, spiritual, and energy body imbalances that are key pieces of the puzzle to rebuild health to a resonance of wellness.

Lyme is a lower disruptive frequency in our bodies, much like other pathogens and health challenges, and to eradicate it and heal from it we must learn to shift our frequency to one of a higher vibration and light than before. We can do this with medications, herbs, thoughts, beliefs, life style changes, physical movement, and much more.

Up and Coming

The second book in the series, *Unlimiting Yourself from Lyme: Identifying the Limiting Factors of Treating Lyme Disease* I will be focusing on physical body healing and challenges more in depth, which is the first side of the "Diamond and Pyramid of Healing Model" introduced in this first book.

The third book in the series will be focusing on the emotional, mental, psychological, and social issues of healing from Lyme disease.

Key Points to Take Away

You Are Powerful. I also want you to know that you are a powerful being and to learn to trust your soul given energy power. You can and will heal. Trusting in ourselves and believing in our innate healing ability is another important part to this journey. We are energy. We are spirit and we are human in this physical body on Earth. The power of our thoughts, our intentions, our prayers, and our beliefs can heal or hurt us. If you learn to trust your inner power, and you find faith in the higher power and combine these two things you can have expedited healing.

Trust Your Body. The human body is an amazing vessel. It knows how to heal itself and given the right support to help it get itself back in balance, back into homeostasis, you can and will start to feel better. Learning to trust our bodies for the amazing work they do and believing in their strength and inner knowing is another part of the puzzle of healing.

Never Underestimate The Power Of Creativity And Joy In Healing. Having a sense of humor about life, seeing and thinking about your healing in ways that bring laughter, joy, and creativity daily will help you heal much faster than if you are stuck in serious mode which is really easy to have happen when you are chronically ill and in pain. We are energy beings and honestly there is unlimited potential because of this. If we get too serious, we start to limit our creativity and optomistic thinking for healing — instead you can become stuck in negative thinking *"I can't, it won't happen, that's not possible."* The limbic system can get stuck in negative loop patterns. These can trap us into being stuck sick. If you can find ways to bring some play, creativity, and laughter into your day it will greatly increase your ability to heal faster.

Using your right brain to visualize yourself getting better and using cartoons or something funny to symbolize it can help. For example when I was healing from Lyme I started doing a visualization that I was a cowboy and I was lassoing the spirochetes hiding in my tissues and organs throughout my body and pulling them out and killing them and gently and easily removing them from my body. I started having a lot of fun with these images. The best part is suddenly the Lyme started to disappear faster with my treatments. I actually became Lyme free on testing soon after I started this process — three months when I say soon. But I had been hitting a wall in treatment and unable to make headway towards killing the Lyme bacteria and this visualization-self hypnosis that I did daily for 10 minutes or more made a huge difference in my body's ability to find the Lyme in my body. It helped activate and awaken my immune system. Plus it made me laugh and smile when I did it, which is the key to healing.

You Have Choice In All You Do. When you are going to doctors and searching for answers and relief remember that no matter what they tell you or say, it's ultimately your choice. You have the power to choose if their advice or treatments or whatever fits you. Its your body. It's your choice always. Never let someone take that from you because in the end it is you who is living in your body not anyone else and you know your body better then anyone else. Trust your gut, trust your intuition on if something is helpful or not, and listen to your inner knowing for guidance on your healing path. For me finding a form of meditation each day helps me hear myself better. It can be a walking meditation, quiet meditation, laying down, sitting up, listening to music, or quiet. Just a way that allows you to connect to your higher self and hear yourself.

Finding Your Purpose. In the healing process it can become quite overwhelming and feel like you are never going to get better. Figuring out what your purpose or focus or dreams are can make all the difference. Having something that you can visualize yourself doing and being when you are better can help give you hope and motivation to get through the hard times in treatment. It is not always an easy journey and the pain and emotions and fear we can experience while treating Lyme can be overwhelming but what I found is once I had my purpose and what I was trying to get to in the end — I was able to push through those hard times a little easier focusing on where I wanted to go next.

My purpose is to help those who are in health challenges feeling confused, lost, and upset about why they are going through what they are and how to get through the challenging and painful times. I want to be a catalyst for their healing through sharing my own story and insights to find the light in the darkness that comes with health challenges like Lyme. I can only reach a limited number of people working one-on-one with clients, so instead I have stepped back from that and focused in on writing books.

While I was struggling with Lyme I was constantly doing research and reading blogs on Lyme. These voices in the Lyme Blogs and books while I was sick really helped give me hope and find my way in the darkness of the treatment journey. I really want to be of service to the light, God. I want to give that hope I received in my darkness to others struggling paying it forward.

Like my friend Rachel and I like to say, "When life gives you Lyme, make lymeade." :)

About the Author

Caroline DeLoreto is a Functional Diagnostic Nutrition-Practitioner (FDN-P), counselor, remote energy practitioner, educator, and inspirational speaker. She has an MA in both Education and Clinical Psychology. Since 2006 she has had a passion for teaching people about their health and how to create the life they desire. She lives happily with her partner in Northern Vermont where she enjoys spending time writing, meditating, studying health, being outside, and walking her labradoodle Lilli in the vibrant green woods of Vermont!

About the Book

From Lyme to Light is my spiritual and physical healing journey with neurological Lyme disease. Starting with a tick bite that led to dementia followed by a stroke and then a Near Death Experience (NDE), I learned how to overcome the confusion and challenges involved with a mysterious illness to find hope and wellness! This book tells my story and shares the Diamond of Healing Philosophy I created to help guide and empower you to find your own healing journey. We are all energy and to heal we must address all aspects of what makes us who we are; the physical body, the mental & emotional body, the social body, and the spirit body. These all come together to make the energy body, which is explained in the Diamond. This book helps you identify potential blocks in your healing and offers some easy to do, affordable, and practical tools to support you on your healing journey. My goal is to empower you and to catalyze your innate ability to heal and maintain wellness far into the future; finding your light from Lyme!